About the Author

CW00555077

Patrice Chaplin is an internation; author who has published more t.......... ......, ... stories. Her most notable work includes *Albany Park, Siesta* – which was made into a film staring Jodi Foster and Isabella Rossellini with music by Miles Davis – *Into the Darkness Laughing, Hidden Star, Night Fishing, Death Trap* and *City of Secrets*.

As a Bohemian in Paris during the 50's and 60's, she spent time with Jean Paul Sartre and Simone de Beauvoir. She was married to Charlie Chaplin's son, Michael, and during her avant-garde journeys through occult circles her friends included Salvador Dali, Jean Cocteau – who gave her a starring role in one of his films – Lauren Bacall, Miles Davis and experts on the esoteric practices of the Kabbalah in Spain.

As an accomplished writer, Patrice has contributed to many collections of short stories, including *Black Valentine* and *The Minerva Book of Short Stories 1*. Her plays, documentaries, and short stories have been extensively written and adapted for radio. The short story *Night in Paris* has been translated in many countries, and other short stories of hers have appeared in magazines and newspapers, including *The Independent*.

Patrice's stage play *From the Balcony* was commissioned by The National Theatre in London in conjunction with BBC Radio 3, and was performed at the Cottesloe Theatre.

Patrice is the director of Northern Bridge Productions, a non-profit organization that leads workshops based in the performing arts as a new and unique way to help fight addiction.

Also by Patrice Chaplin

FICTION:
A Lonely Diet
By Flower and Dean Street
The Last of the Big Kite Flyers
Having It Away
Siesta
The Unforgotten
Don Salino's Wife
The Fame People
Forget Me Not
Saraband
Night Fishing: An Urban Tale
Death Trap
Mr. Lazarus
The Fortune Seller
Lucifer By Moonlight

NON-FICTION:
Cry, Wolf
Another City
Albany Park: An Autobiography
Into the Darkness Laughing
Hidden Star: Oona O'Neill Chaplin: a Memoir
Happy Hour
Cleopatra: The Story of an Obsession
Clean Time
City of Secrets
The Portal
The Stone Cradle: One Woman's Search for the
Truth Beyond Everyday Reality
The Unknown Pursuit: Three Grandmothers in
Search of the Grail

AN EPISODIC AUTOBIOGRAPHY

HOLLYWOOD TO KENTISH TOWN

PATRICE CHAPLIN

Quadrant Books

Copyright © 2024 by Patrice Chaplin

First published in 2024 by Quadrant Books

The right of Patrice Chaplin to be identified as the Author of the Work
has been asserted by her in accordance with the Copyright, Designs and
Patents Act 1988.

All rights reserved. No part of this publication may be reproduced,
stored in a retrieval system, or transmitted, in any form or by any means,
without the prior permission in writing of the author, nor be otherwise
circulated in any form of binding or cover other than that in which it is
published and without a similar condition including this condition being
imposed on the subsequent purchaser.

ISBN: 978-1-7384598-3-4

This book is produced in association with Northern Bridge Productions
Charity No. 1077637

Quadrant Books

Published by Quadrant Books

Suite 2,
7 Dyer Street, Cirencester,
Gloucestershire, GL7 2PF
T: 020 3290 0920
www.quadrant-books.com
info@quadrant-books.com

CONTENTS

CHAPTER 1

THERE WAS NOT A ROOM to be had in NYC except for just one in a hotel off Broadway. In the cab driver's opinion it was not the sort of address a woman on her own would choose even in an emergency. My agent's assistant had sounded a little reticent about her choice but it was my first visit to the city and I was already high on its dynamic uprush. New York was 'on' day and night and I could feel the elated energy throbbing up from the sidewalk. It suited me from my first moment. I could handle anything.

I had arrived at JFK on the Red Eye night flight from LA to start work on my first film. It was the end of the 1960s and a producer had liked my science fiction book 'Blue Suburb' and a deal had been put together. I would collaborate with him on the first draft script in his lively downtown apartment. On arrival at the hotel one look suggested the film could be low budget.

The Taft was huge, old, with over 2,500 rooms and had known better times. Unmodernised by design or lack of money it belonged to another era and the present day crowd lining up to try for a vacancy had nothing to do with the spirit of the place. Opened in 1926 and renamed The Taft after a former US president it had once been a venue of standing, famous for the big bands playing nightly and broadcast nationwide on radio. There were still touches from that earlier time. Brass elevator doors, Art Deco chandeliers, the spacious gleaming foyer like a dance floor which it had once been. Along one wall grilled windows from the 1920s kept the receptionists separate from the general public. As I was already booked in I was told to join a superior reserved section where men waited in lines and the lines were long. Most were down at heel with an out of town appearance, used to standing in queues ending nowhere. The place was becoming airless. It didn't look as though much was superior here. A man behind me said most were waiting for the chance of a vacancy. 'It used to be a swell place. All the dance bands played here. Glen Miller.' He carried a sax, a drum and had been on the road for days. He needed a room just for a few hours to freshen up for that night's gig down in the Village. He was happy to share with any of the guys and split the cost. I asked if I was in the queue for reserved. The man in front turned surprised I was there. 'What you doing in a spot like this, where do you come from. You sound top drawer to me.'

'She's from good old London Town.' And the musician pushed his luggage forward. The man in front wearing his jacket in spite of the heat had to keep up appearances. 'You belong uptown.'

'No rooms uptown,' said the musician.

The overdressed man decided he had to explain himself and wiped his sweating head with a morbid handkerchief. 'I am in town on business and I mean the money markets and I'm queueing here because every room in Manhattan is taken. There's not one convention in town but three. It's either this dump or a bench in Penn Station or the cemetery.' His hat stuck to the back of his head defying gravity.

'You're a man that can spot alternatives,' said the musician.

'I never thought I would end up in The Taft.'

'Well this young lady from London Town is here. No-one comes here. They just end up here.' He told me the clubs he had played in London and had had a meaningful career.

'Three conventions and nowhere to lay my head. And I've been coming to this city all my life. Why should I be queuing with a lot of losers,' said the businessman.

Others had the same story. For a moment they all looked about the same. Is that what being closed in with a crowd on the wrong side of luck did to you?

'It's that short-sighted mayor,' said the businessman. 'Who the hell voted for him? I might as well lie down in the cemetery. At least it's got air.'

'I wish you wouldn't keep talking about graveyards.' The man was shaky and nondescript. 'That's one thing I would never do. I would rather be dead.'

'You've got that right,' said the businessman.

I realised a scrawny unwashed youth beside me was touching my thigh as he tried to unzip my bag. I dealt with the crime problem by going to the desk in the middle of the hall. Here the under manager sat on a high stool, cool and remote from the foyer chaos. Maybe it was the lonely job that gave him the cold arrogant expression. I said his clients were giving me a hard time.

'That's life. Go back to the queue or you'll lose your reservation.'

*

I'd been part of that queue for nearly an hour. Maybe that was part of the life he was talking about. I decided to give it another few minutes then call the agent.

An old fan hung from the high ceiling and spun pointlessly. A woman pushed ahead of me and wanted the immediate release of her jewellery from the hotel safe. A few women, some still sporting the trappings of the night were sprinkled along the queues, their fake jewels askew, the stale perfume transformed by the heat to its cheap origins. Not usually seen by the light of day these women had arrived through some misfortune which resulted in this grim queue.

The line shifted forward and men in shoes polished bright for another luckless day lifted again their one piece of luggage which in some cases probably contained their entire worldly goods.

The clerk behind the grill, and I was beginning to see why they needed all that protection, refused the jewel seeking woman anything until she paid her bill.

'But I have sir.' She clung to the bars.

'You owe an extra day m'am. We've been through this already.'

'I was due to leave this morning but my husband died up there.'

The queueing men did not know what to make of that. One murmured to those behind him that she had given the guy too much fun and it killed him. 'You can be too old even for that.'

The clerk refused to open the safe. 'Maybe he died but you still didn't vacate the room before 10 so I have to charge you an extra day plus city tax.'

'How could I vacate the room sir?'

'What about insurance?' said the businessman now down to his shirt. 'I can always get her some of that.'

'Not her thing.' The new voice certainly unusual belonged in better places. He was another who didn't fit The Taft. His words were beautifully delivered with a certain pleasure. He looked educated, expressive, with an inner elegance that surely belonged uptown wherever that was.

The musician nudged me. 'Maybe the heat is getting to me but I am sure that is Silvio Narizzano the movie director.'

'You can be anything in this place,' said a new companion.

The musician was still excited. 'This director has just got an Emmy for his last film. What is he doing here?'

The smart stranger left the queue and stood apart taking in the scene from every angle. He had a definite presence and was accustomed to the best side of life. His clothes were simple, elegant, his shoes were of the best brand. Hair well cut and he was clean. What was he doing here? In his mid-forties, quick thinking, he was used to making decisions. Maybe the musician was right and he was a well known director. He was a lot of other things too but I didn't know it then.

'Just walk out lady,' he told the woman. She did turn to check him out.

'I'll come with you,' he said.

'I bet you would,' said the businessman pushing his way nearer to the front.

'Then she'd really need insuring.'

'I'll put you in a cab for the women's refuge,' said the smart stranger. And he tried to take her away. 'No good fighting with reception. They're only doing their job. Same old script. The refuge can't be worse than this.'

'But you're in it,' said the businessman.

'I take it as it comes.'

I was surprised he was so easygoing with this crowd. He held their attention with his next best choice for the woman. She should sue them. That got a laugh. This smart stranger belonged in places of his own choice. He was in trouble because he liked it. I could see he could get away with bad outcomes. He got the queue's attention off the heat.

'What are you? Robin Hood?' asked a crumpled man.

'He died here didn't he? He was alive enough when he arrived. Let them deal with it. Look after yourself.' And then the smart stranger got the queue's undivided attention as he handed the woman a sheaf of money, all high value notes. The men gasped and some wanted to help her count it.

Some said, run for it. The smart stranger was ahead of that. 'She needs her papers and ID. They won't release anything without being paid.' He looked at the woman. 'You won't go far without your papers.'

'What business you in?' asked the businessman.

'Getting safes open.'

He turned to the woman. 'Now pay your bill.'

The banknotes had already slipped safe into some part of her underclothes.

All on her own she was considering other options. They did include making a run for it. Out of the two kinds of trouble the woman was in she preferred the lack of money. She told Robin Hood to buzz off and paid the extra for the room.

'But you wanted to take care of your husband,' said the businessman.

'He can die all he wants. I just want my jewels.'

The men relaxed now they knew what she was and what they were dealing with.

'So how do you feel now Robin Hood?' said the guy who wouldn't sleep in cemeteries.

The smart stranger suddenly clapped his hands and laughed. 'It's the best story I've heard all week.'

'She just wants her trinkets,' said the businessman.

The woman saw security guys closing in. The men watched as she tap tapped her way to the exit on shoes, one higher than the other and not hers.

Then the smart stranger's eyes met mine and he looked happy. 'I love this place.'

The musician joined in. 'What are you doing here? You were on a roll. Things can't have gone bad that quick. The Emmy and all.'

The smart stranger laughed. 'I told you I love this place. Nowhere like it.'

I suddenly spoke. 'You don't like things too predictable.'

'And I don't mind paying for it.' He spun around and went across to the soft drink machine and came back with two cartons which he gave to me and the musician. Then he walked light and free to the exit like someone having the right kind of day.

'He's classy,' said the musician. And we agreed he loved this place.

CHAPTER 2

IT WAS A LONG WALK to the under manager's desk, space all around him. 'It's good you don't suffer from agoraphobia,' I told him. He wasn't sure what that was and asked what I wanted. I told him. His mild blue eyes took in good, bad, just as it came and his smile, on for the duration of his shift, did the rest.

A shelf arrangement above his head was held up by two poles and piled with bundles of mail, rolled newspapers and packages, all dusty. As he spoke a worn envelope sailed down from the pile on the shelf and stuck like a dart in his thick fake waved hair. He flicked it away and it continued to the floor. It looked old. I picked it up and saw it was addressed to John Deer Esq., care of The Taft and dated 1947. The under manager barely looked at it and threw it in the bin.

My agent arrived breathless and took my bag. 'But this is The Taft! What are you thinking of?' I reminded him his assistant had made the booking.

'You will be better at The Chelsea with Quentin and Hunke.' He was referring to the anarchic Quentin Crisp, creator of 'The Naked Civil Servant.' Herbert Hunke was one of the legendary US Beat characters from the 50s.

'The Chelsea? Full!,' said the under manager without prejudice.

A man left the queue and asked if there was any mail for him. The under manager barely raised his eyes to the untidy heap above him. 'No post.' The agent said he'd go and get me a proper hotel.

'This town is tighter than Fort Knox. Take the room unseen and have a shower,' said the under manager. 'And your agent will get you the illusive somewhere that doesn't exist today.'

Maybe he should be my agent.

He produced a huge gilt key. 'It's the only bed you'll get in the Big Apple. Keep your door locked at all times and the chain on.'

*

The room was top of the range with shower. It was seedy. It was the nth degree of seediness. People had died there and would go on dying there. I distrusted everything about it. I was to find that New York was a flamboyant mixture of super modern and everything else. I dialled room service and ordered coffee, pancake and juice. I then tried to get the air-con to work. The window was barely a slit in the wall its view an airshaft. I rang room service and they said my order was on its way. I picked up the over handled plastic menu and ordered a portion of fries. Another man took over and for a moment I thought it was the one they called Silvio Narizzano. It was surely the same voice. He said, 'I recommend today's special.'

I asked what it was.

'You.'

I could hear laughter around him. He hung up.

The bathroom floor was a mixture of dark Lino congested with dirt and it stuck to my bare feet. The plastic tiling greasy. The towel was the size of a large handkerchief but it hadn't been used. The knock on the door was officious and I opened it eager for the coffee. Two security guards stood disapproving.

'Never open your door. Keep it locked and on the chain.' He pointed to the various signs from all ages on the back of the door. One message. Danger. 'Always ask who's there.'

I said I was waiting for room service which still hadn't arrived.

'That's called Waiting for Godot.' The guards strolled off laughing.

I sat on the very edge of the bed and phoned the agent but the number did not go through. A recorded female voice informed me outside calls were not allowed on this service. What room was I in? What about the dead man's room. Had he been lying here unattended for hours? I snapped shut my luggage and walked the endless corridor to the lift.

In the foyer I phoned my friend Alan Brien the film critic on The Sunday Times as agreed and gave him an update of my New York project. He thought the fee was modest but it was my first script writing job. He asked where I was staying.

'Not somewhere you'd know.'

'The Taft!' He was delighted. He not only knew it, he had stayed there when he was starting his career. 'I booked in for a week but I had to stay 6 months. It was the cheapest deal around. I never made enough money to check out. I was broke, lonely, too young and not even my family wrote to me. I didn't hear from anyone. Not even the few who'd said they'd sent me money. And one day as I stopped at the under manager's desk and as usual there were never any letters for me, I noticed this ever increasing stack of mail on a shelf above his head. I asked who it was for. He could not be bothered to reach up and used to chuck the letters up above his head and mostly they landed on that pile.' And Alan described how one day he noticed a package with English stamps. 'I climbed up there and discovered 6 months mail, most of it for me. Just for the fun of it go and ask if there is any left over for me. 15 years ago.'

Alan had no bitter memories of that time. 'It was a marvellous place, The Taft. An institution. They had the big

9

bands every night with their signature tune, 'Love letters in the sand'. It was a favourite place in the 30s and 40s. The Roxy Theatre was part of the building. Glamour show business.' I looked around the foyer. Not today.

'The Taft is a piece of history. You're lucky.'

Firstly I told the under manager I could not stay and complained about the room service. He was puzzled. 'But we don't have room service m'am.' He pointed to a coffee shop at the side of the hotel. 'That's all the service we've got.'

I asked who answered the room service call and took orders when there was no service. He thought I was another nut. 'Lady, just get a coffee from the coffee shop. It doesn't belong to us.' That at least was a recommendation. Then Silvio Narizzano's face rested briefly in my thoughts. Could it be him who answers the calls? Did he run the room service? I described the man who could be Silvio. He did pause. 'Yes I have heard of someone of that description.'

'Living here?'

'Visiting.' He was eager to change the subject.

So he knew he also could have a bad day I asked for letters for Alan Brien the well known film critic.

'Not today.' He didn't even look up at the shelf.

'15 years ago.'

'We've never been a delivery service.'

In the coffeeshop I had a good all day breakfast while waiting for the agent. I had no idea what time it was. The waiter told me room service had stopped years ago. He also mentioned a wayward part with people living in one corner of the hotel, just squatting there, a whole colony mostly on poor relief. Some had been there for years and closed the area off. 'No-one dares to go up there. Not even the police.' I asked if he'd seen them. 'I see their washing hanging over balconies. Perhaps they run room service.'

I described Silvio Narizzano and how it could have been him answering the phone service.

'Yes I've heard of this man. He comes to and fro. They say he runs the squat.'

I was leaving with my agent to stay with a friend of his when the under manager handed me an envelope. It was dated 1939 and inside was a rhyme.

A handless man a letter did write.
A dumb one dictated it word for word.
The man who read it had lost his sight.
And deaf was he who listens and heard.

It summed up The Taft postal service.

A few years later I heard The Taft had been closed down due to lack of upkeep attracting unattractive elements. It had recently been turned into luxury apartments. But whenever afterwards I mentioned The Taft no-one knew exactly where it once was or if it had ever been.

But I had met the smart stranger Silvio Narizzano by then.

CHAPTER 3

HE PROPOSED MARRIAGE CROSSING A motorway in North London. In spite of the speeding vehicles we arrived, not without danger, onto the small traffic island in the middle of the thoroughfare which we should never have crossed in the first place. But that was Silvio Narizzano. Why choose the safety of a zebra crossing when a short distance away you were offered a challenge to your very being. Four lines of vehicles sped in a frenzy north and south and the island not spacious in the first place seemed to shrink as I clung to its unserviceable bit of railing.

I couldn't hear what Silvio said at first. Then I thought two of the words might have been 'Marry me.' Naturally I laughed. Horns blaring as a bus and a car almost collided meant I had to shout my answer. 'I thought you asked me to marry you.' I waited for him to laugh.

'You'd better had,' he shouted back. He didn't look at me as though disowning this nonsensical spur of the moment suggestion. Again I laughed. He didn't like that.

'Marry?' I said. 'Maybe you're allergic to the petrol.'

'I want to help bring up your son. He needs a father.'

It would take him to see that. Having known him for nearly

three years I could think of a dozen obstacles to the very idea without even trying. The shrinking island in the tumult of speeding metal seemed to sum up not just the act of marriage to Silvio but the fight for survival afterwards.

From this island there was escape when the lights further along finally turned red. But for the island in the domestic tempest there were no outside controlling signs that directed and made it all finally safe.

He spoke. 'I was born against a red light. Couldn't wait for it to turn green.' Like a magician he shimmied off the island and weaved through skidding traffic reaching the other side with ease. I could see no solution for me. Clinging with damp hands to the faulty railing, vertigo beginning. It took minutes to trust the red light enough to step into the slight pause provided and cross in front of cars raring to go. He was gone. He could accept the rejection. But never forgive the laughter.

*

Alan Brien just off the plane from Nice rushed straight to my place in Kentish Town, still carrying his luggage. His eyes were actually glowing as he hurried across the spacious 1860s tessellated hallway. They knew how to lay out a hall in those days. The staircase banisters were effortlessly beautiful. Obviously Alan had finished my book and something significant had occurred. Straight back from the Cannes Festival he hadn't even stopped at his own home where his journalist wife, the much applauded Jill Tweedie would be cooking dinner. Had he shown my book to someone of importance. Alan the well known film critic on the Sunday Times had enough pull to get things done.

'So you've read it Alan. I know the beginning still needs—' I chose 'work.' Eyes fixed on the distant kitchen, he pushed past the dogs. I followed him across the sparse living room little changed since the 1920s. Was my book that good? I was daring to be a little happy. A deal from Cannes could change my life.

'I'm too late.' Alan sounded concerned. The room was empty except for a lopsided table and various chairs and Silvio Narizzano lying out of sight in the best one. 'Don't tell me I've missed him,' said Alan. The elder dog growled. She was not a fan of excited guests. Or Alan.

'There you are!' And Alan rushed towards Silvio and shook his hand. 'Jill thought you would be here.'

And then I understood his unexpected visit had nothing much to do with me. Alan got himself a can of beer from the kitchen and a coke for Silvio then pulled up a reliable looking stool. 'It's like The Taft in the old days isn't it. Being here. That's why I like it.'

'It has a certain charm,' said Silvio deciding to be cautious for once. He might need to stay in this Taft-like dump. As I understood he had been thrown out of his own home.

'It was wonderful,' said Alan.

Silvio didn't bother to sit up. 'The Taft? Or Cannes?'

'You. You're up for the Palmes D'Or. You'll get that. The movie will be a smash in the States.'

And Alan spoke without stop of the industry approval Silvio's film had claimed.

So he had come to see the recalcitrant guest. My book was quite forgotten.

Silvio didn't give much reaction. I knew he was torn between directing a series of three plays for Laurence Olivier on TV or making a film 'Staying On' in India. He simply got Alan's mind off the Cannes subject by telling him the plot of another film he wanted to make and needed to raise the money. He was good at getting you away from what he didn't currently care about. 'I can pull it in at a million and a half.'

'Some deferred payments there,' said Alan automatically.

Jill arrived and whisked Silvio around to her place for a roast dinner. She was hoping for an interview for The Guardian or The New Statesman.

And that was how it became in Kentish Town. People might

come to see me but they hoped to meet Silvio.

My book had some good reviews. It was a true story that Alan and Jill insisted I write. They even found me a publisher. I was invited onto a publicity show that I couldn't handle. Yes or no was the best I could do.

Finally it was the critic from The Times that told me I had to expand my answers. Maybe yes and no worked on radio but I should be doing the big stuff on TV. 'There's a popular show in Birmingham. Writers would give anything to be on that. I can get you on. It will change your status, give you a career. On my paper you will be noticed but you'll only get half a page.'

'But it's The Times.'

'You're lucky if you get 10,000 reading this interview. TV in Birmingham gives you a 100,000 viewers. Think of the sales. The publishers will love you.'

'A recorded show naturally.'

'Live,' she said.

'Impossible.'

'Take a couple of pills and a drink and go for it.'

I reminded her I didn't do all that for my first book.

"Blue Suburb' was okay but you got the attention because you were new. A second book is much harder to push. Birmingham is a huge career chance. They will all want you. You're a natural.' She was no fortune-teller.

Her persistence got me north. The show's producer had promised me a lot including being filmed exterior in the street. Just him and me and the camera. No audience.

Audience? That was a new horror. Where was this?

'In the studio. Not that you would notice. A good way from where you sit.' He thought he had got the better of what he believed was just the normal, nerves of a first timer and gave up on all the half promises and private street scenes that didn't exist anyway.

Bananarama, the new band had just been on. They recognised me from Kentish Town and loved the fact I was hiding in the lavatory. They didn't believe the 'just a quick pee' story. They climbed up the walls hands filled with half drunk bottles of liquor, spliffs and pills. 'Take the lot and get out there and show them. They're only Brummies. We are Kentish Town and right behind you.'

The actor John Hurt's wife was due to follow me. She looked composed and ready for anything. I sat sideways to the interviewer at a small table. To the left the audience was a large wave inescapable washing in towards me.

At first the interviewer tried to play with the audience. He just had Bananarama and hadn't quite settled down.

'Tell us what you felt when you first saw the Spaniard and you a girl of 15.'

He didn't expect the silence that followed. Nor did I.

Remember to make them laugh. Alan had told me that. No chance of that. Now the questions were fast. What would Silvio do? I closed my eyes and thought of him. He'd get up and join the audience. He'd dismantle the whole thing and make this his own show and be brilliant and the audience would love him. He'd do what he wanted but I wasn't Silvio. He was away filming in Canada.

After some moments the interviewer suddenly stopped talking. He sat mute as though he'd caught my stage fright. The production team prepared for such an emergency speedily showed images of me at 15 and the Spanish lover. When I did speak I made yes and no sound like Shakespeare. 'Any questions?' The producer had suddenly spoken.

'Do you have a nurse nearby?' I replied. I'd forgotten we were on speaker. The Brummie audience loved it. They laughed. They shouted. She wants a nurse. They thought it was a joke. No joke. I was ready to flop out. I looked at the interviewer. 'You told me there was no audience.'

More Brummie laughter. 'We've given London girl the wobblies. We're too much for these down south chicks.' That was the most acceptable remark from that audience. And then the Bananarama girls were out there mauling the audience. They showed them what girls down south could do. The chaos that followed was cut. My interviewer was cut and so was I.

No more being clever on air.

But the Bananarama girls loved it. They thought I was great. Done the show my way. Nothing wrong with that.

When Silvio heard about it he had all the answers. 'What's the matter with you? Just lead the conversation. Say something you feel safe with and get him to pick it up.'

The trouble – there was nothing safe. I had to remember he had got all sorts of actors through the nerves and troubles of their early days. Anthony Hopkins in his first film. Dennis Hopper trying to stay off drink. Terrence Stamp, even Tallulah Bankhead in the nerves of her later years.

When I left RADA I thought I might end up on the stage. But all I ended up with was stage fright.

CHAPTER 4

LOOKING BACK THE CAT CAME into the house about the same time as Silvio. I did accuse him later of bringing her in to cause yet more drama. He couldn't scoff enough. 'Bring her in? What do you think she is? She gets in.'

I decided the boys let her in.

'She doesn't bother with doorways. She climbs up that Sycamore at the end of the garden and runs along the neighbours' walls. I've seen her get up the drainpipe to the first floor gutter. Someone must open the landing window. She's not called The Cat for nothing.'

He seemed to like her.

'You seem to know a lot about it. Is that how you get in places where you're no longer wanted?'

I thought I had seen The Cat coming down from the attic rooms. One thing I began to notice was that she liked to remain unseen. She was more a presence than an actual figure. I thought I saw her near the front door. She seemed to rely on shadows.

The gang of Kentish Town boys that met high up the stairway on the third floor would never let a girl into their world. They did know her name and thought she was 13. She didn't go to school. The boys aged between 11 and 14 came from all classes and backgrounds. Two or three came from smart homes and went to private schools but sought what their privileged parents could not give them. They needed the street cred of being associated with the gang. Others came from broken homes or no homes. Davis the dealer slept on benches or in the laundrette. He was 14 and wanted to get straight and be in a band. His face was covered with scars from fights with rival dealers and customers who didn't pay. The pickpocket Ace had been in every children's home and care centre in the area and felt the only place that worked for him was the third floor landing. The others went to Hampstead Comp or Chalk Farm.

My sons had two rooms just below the attic. Tom's was a chaos beyond redemption. He liked to draw and paint and was considered 'sometimes extraordinary.' He went to a variety of schools and disliked the lot. Just turned 12 he had a light and noticeable walk, his feet soundless and gentle on the pavement. Even then he had a certain allure. James, 13, kept his room clear with everything clean and put away. Oddly the gang preferred to hang out in the orderly room. Maybe keeping his drum kit in there had something to do with it. Silvio preferred either room as long as he could be part of the action. He was the only adult who got in and only for the shortest time. They had just discovered Karaoke and Ace had a wonderful voice with a high range and could sing anything. Jill's son Luke got the gang doing a Karaoke show in the garden of the old Assembly Rooms pub and other offers came in. Music took over their lives. Before I reached my iron outer gate I could hear the drums, smell the dope. Again I asked the boys about The Cat and they denied ever seeing her. Then Tom pretended to realise who I meant. 'Oh she doesn't stay here. Not for the night.' He looked at his older brother for support. James was the one with the answers and occasionally came up with something hard to challenge.

I said I wanted to know who she was. Never mind where she slept. 'Doesn't she go to Anna Scher's,' James decided. A good choice. Anna was the famous children's drama teacher and some of the boys went on Tuesday night. That would put The Cat in good favour with adults.

'She could even be an actress,' said Tom. 'She could even be Silvio's daughter. She looks like him.' He had taken it too far. They the boys laughed themselves to the last gasp.

I didn't believe any of it. Then.

Of course she brought the dope. That was it. I went back downstairs and crossed the spacious landing to Steve's workroom. He was my companion, lover and best friend. He had the entire first floor with its magnificent high windows and moulded rosettes in the ceiling. His books filled the front room of this private space. Silvio occasionally got in there. Steve taught philosophy at the Poly in Kentish Town. He looked like Bob Dylan and was popular with his students. He was considered the teacher to go to. Before I even mentioned The Cat I knew he would be on her side. He was liberal except with people who weren't.

'The Cat?' He had never seen her. 'What's the problem?'

'As long as she doesn't become pregnant,' I answered, my mind full of even worse.

Silvio seeing the door open came in and they sat, the two men, to have a good and energetic discussion about the new philosophy movement. I realised Silvio could fit in with any person, any group. And he genuinely brought valid points of view. He fitted in this book-filled study as well as he did on the third floor with the drums.

My old beautiful house was large enough to be generous and people drawn by its atmosphere asked to stay. One said it felt like a loving parent. I felt good things had happened here. The garden was untouched and spread with rarely seen wild flowers that came from a previous time. The house, sparsely furnished kept its strong character. The area itself was untouched and children still played in the wide street. All attempts at modernisation were discouraged. The area had somehow missed being selected for exploitation. The house, bought in 1974 had cost the exorbitant figure of £17,000.

Norman the traveller came to stay. Unusually attractive he was used to the differing effects he had on people from adoration to jealousy to disbelief. If they couldn't own him they could doubt his existence and stir this doubt in others. He was not willing to be classified but had obviously had a past. He had worked for The Economist and The Spectator. His brother in Melbourne was an established academic. It seemed after certain governmental positions Norman quit the lot and chose to travel. He'd been everywhere but the people he met in those new places were always ones with influence and power. He was bright, well educated but it was as though he carried a whole part of himself as a secret and it would never be discovered and he'd defend it to the last.

People were often unsure of him. He covered himself with opinions and they were well presented and usually correct. He said he was a traveller. He invented a life that fitted into a rucksack and crossed deserts. Then it came out that his university lecturer brother was CIA and had probably recruited him.

Finally I said, 'Norman, what do you actually do?'

He replied immediately. 'I thought you knew. I am someone who does not like direct questions.' He pointed to the floor in the downstairs lavatory that he had just tiled. 'That's what I do.'

It was undeniably well done. I was relieved. 'So you tile floors?' No wonder he didn't want people to know. He didn't answer. I leaned down and ran a hand over the tiles. The surface was smooth and perfect.

'That's what I do,' he said. 'I make things smooth.'

He undoubtedly could foresee global financial outcomes and when we gathered around the black and white TV for the news he'd get most predictions right. I got the feeling he didn't like any of it and the travelling was his spiritual survival. When Silvio met him he said, 'Why do you all make such a fuss? All this 'what does he do?' Nothing. And nothing is what he does.'

Norman brought an English performer Charlotte into the house. She walked tightropes in theatres and clubs in Paris and naked in the ones in Las Vegas. She had a wonderful deep voice and a style that stirred up any neighbourhood. Everything about her, the shoes, the beret, the earrings, all made a point. It was all part of her life performance. She was top drawer English but preferred performing in Paris and was no stranger to the darker side of that life. She was someone who's values Norman totally approved of. And he enjoyed her dry wit and inside stories. He called her Bad Girl. I was definitely a ground floor person and I liked the proximity of the garden and the street. I could open the front door and go right to the corner shop or left to the airport and New York. Nobody could explain the house. It led to another existence, a realm where better things happen.

I told Norman I had to go back to New York. He said he loved it here and felt better and healed. It was as though he had even surprised himself.

Silvio bought the boys a car. The only thing was it didn't start.

'Trust you mister cheap,' I said. 'It doesn't move.'

'Of course not,' he replied. 'They can't drive. They're not even 15.' Just in case I didn't get it he said you had to be 18 to drive.

'So what do they do with it?'

'They sit in it and dream.'

For weeks the car stayed outside the main gate. Then the boys moved it round to the side road. They spent time washing it, cleaning it, understanding its workings. They tried to repair it. At some point they even tried to sell it. People could sit in it by invitation. It became the gang hub. A Honda, third hand, 20 years old with phenomenal miles on the clock. Luke mended the door and kept it clean. They had it valued. But only a miracle would have that working. And Silvio was the miracle. One summer night he filled the tank, piled it with kids, started the croaking engine and took them up the M1 as far as Bedford and back.

'So how did you do that?' I asked. 'Magic?'

He shook a set of keys. 'Don't tell them.'

By the autumn, covered with fallen leaves from the Sycamore it was forgotten. By winter it had been towed away. It had been a vehicle of dreams.

Then came the skateboarding, the graffiti nights, and the football.

*

Overnight every wall in Kentish Town had an elaborate painted sign with the letters PW. Some were in chalk. I asked what it meant and how it got there. I didn't have to look far.

'Private World,' said James matter of fact. After a pause Tom added, 'It's ours.'

I thought Tom was only responsible for graffiti filling the walls by the station. Tom had extended his wall as far as Camden High Street. And so according to Luke, Banksy had been to see it. Rami the youngest boy said, 'PW is ours. We are defining our territory. We are now a gang hard to join.'

'So where is PW?' I asked.

'Here.'

'In this house?'

'On the stairs,' said Rami.

'Who runs it?'

'Silvio mostly.'

All this new gang owner would say was it beat watching television.

I knew they would grow out of it. The skateboards came next. But I needed to know what they were doing and why. So I had answers for the official people if it came to that.

James was good at football and already selected to train with a London youth team. He used to kick a ball against a street wall with the Cole brothers, one of who turned into a star Arsenal player. James had won a place at a grammar school and was still considered to be the one with the answers. He was said to have girlfriends.

Both my sons came from a broken family. Their pain and past fitted perfectly into the third floor gang.

The girl was back. I smelt the perfume on the narrow stairs going up to the attic. Silvio had made his home there. He had taken copies of old sheet music covers which had belonged to my mother and decorated his walls. He'd taken something from every corner of the house. He wanted to create a quick atmosphere as he was never sure of his tenure. Silvio put me wise to The Cat.

'She works stations. Especially Kings Cross.'

I wasn't sure which one of all the possibilities he meant.

He said, 'Pickpocket.'

How stupid did I have to be?

'And sometimes goes with a guy.'

'She's 13!' I shouted.

'So was Cleopatra when she went to Rome and seduced what she needed. Life is cheap. Death comes fast. You have to cram a lot in these days.'

CHAPTER 5

CALDON, MY EX-HUSBAND'S BEST friend got married at a registry office in Marylebone Road. Not for him the exuberance of wealth to suit the occasion that would have been provided by his illustrious family. Not to celebrate him. They'd given up on that. But for the bride he was fortunate enough to bind in marriage. His family wanted a wedding recognised and admired globally beyond the confines of the UK. They waited for the arrangements to be passed to them in New York and Israel. They expected the synagogue to be involved. The day came but they knew nothing about it. They were spared.

I knew I was not invited but my ex-husband had already arrived. I did notice that the Kentish Town boys, gathered by the front door looked different. Their hair was combed and in some cases glossed, their clothes pressed, shoes cleaned. James carried a sizeable bunch of flowers. Single file the 15 or more boys stepped gracefully up the path to the road. Steve ran down the stairs and gave Tom a handful of money. 'For afterwards.'

In single file they turned into the high street, this mixed group of boys, all washed and walking proud. They stopped traffic. People took photos, asked questions but the boys carried on walking with a mission and were joined by others, some wearing bowties. Dressed up and confident they followed Caldon south to the Marylebone Road. There were over 70 boys when they arrived at the registry office. My ex-husband had waited with the bride-to-be. Had they expected this display?

Caldon put the ring on his new wife's finger and the cheering and clapping broke out. They were prouder than any groom.

The after ceremony took place in the massive Pizza Palace on Baker Street.

'I have never been so proud.' They all said the same.

Was it Caldon's idea? 'Why not?' he said. 'These kids are the people I care most about. It was marvellous.'

All it needed was Silvio.

'But he was there. He was the best man.'

My former husband Mikey, wearing a white three-piece suit which accentuated his tan drove up in a German car that the Kentish Town boys gathered around and said had belonged to Hitler.

Mikey agreed. It was the same type but not the actual car. His hair was long and lustrous and the hours of meditation, jazz and yoga had done no harm. He had spent the summer in the Caribbean. I spent mine trying to keep my son Tom in the private school and keeping drugs out of the house. This included barring all possible dealers and imposing a strict nocturnal return home upon which pocket money depended.

The worst thing that happened to me that summer was lack of earnings to pay the private school. And Tom's constantly refusing to stay there.

The worst thing that happened to my former husband was a sting from a jellyfish.

'I swam too far out but the ocean was perfect.' It seemed he was accompanied by one or two movie actors.

If he had my life he wouldn't be swimming anywhere and would be spared the stinging jellyfish.

He stood by the garden door brimming with health. He had been blessed by the summer. He was here for one reason. To check on the rumours about his youngest son on the instructions of his mother. But Tom was no fool and stayed hiding upstairs. Then it occurred to me Mikey might be persuaded to persuade his son to stay in the safety of the private school so James got him down into the kitchen. How was it between them? Awkward. Mikey had remarried and had a new family. I held onto the kitchen sink while Mikey admired the dogs. 'They're real dogs.'

I wished he was a real father. I vowed to keep my mouth shut.

'How you doing?' his father asked not expecting an answer. So after the pause my mouth opened and out came the chorus of complaints.

'So what's the problem?' he asked Tom.

Tom managed a downpour of tears which I must say was rare. He begged to be freed from the boarding school. I immediately responded with why he should stay.

Mikey moved away from the garden door and rattled the car keys. This was not his scene. Remotely. This wasn't blue ocean and jellyfish.

'You're upsetting your mother.' Mikey thought he might do something with that observation. 'She's got a point.'

The tears turned to sobs . . . he begged to be freed from the bondage. He was lonely. He had no friends.

'Bullshit. I've read your diary. I know you sell stuff to other kids at 7pm in the schoolyard.' I got on my knees on the kitchen floor and told Mikey to keep his son in that school. It was his one chance.

Of course I should have remembered Mikey had never stayed in a school in his life. He had been to nearly every school for boys in Switzerland. Briefly. He hated school.

He cleared his throat. His voice was still attractive and mid-Atlantic.

'I think Tom can find his own school.'

I was still on my knees and now my hands were clasped

together. 'If he leaves that school it will be the end of him.'

'Which school do you want to go to?' Mikey adopted a fatherly tone. 'Well, none.' At least Tom was honest. Mikey liked that answer.

'If you have to go just for a bit longer–'

'Haverstock,' said Tom immediately. His tears had miraculously dried up.

'Then Haverstock it will be,' said Mikey. He also liked the idea it was free.

'Then he's lost.' I got up slowly from the floor.

I said, 'Haverstock produces the local drugs. If the wind is right you can smell them from here.'

Tom went to Haverstock. Tom was no stranger to lost.

And my former husband walked out smooth as hell to his car. How I wished Silvio was there.

*

Alan told me about The Taft. Of course I had seen Silvio there in that chaotic queue. He was known as Angel of the Gutter. He had been trying to assist the recently widowed woman whose possible husband had been lying dead in the room. And the management would not return her jewels. Was it 4 years ago?

'There's a no-go area in that hotel,' Alan explained. 'The squatters were there. Doggedly present. You could see their washing hanging aired by the winds from the Hudson River. It was called Angel Wing and no-one would choose to go there. Not even the police. Don't forget I was there 6 months because I couldn't get out. Occasionally there was the sound of a woman singing. It made everything seem better. I think she was Dolly Dawn singing The Taft signature tune, 'Love Letters In The Sand.' The Taft on Madison connected to the Roxy Theatre. Dolly Dawn sang in The Taft Grill and then it was broadcast on CBS. You must remember Tommy Dorsey, Artie Shaw, Glenn Miller?

'Yes Alan. Even I remember those.'

'It was said Silvio or someone like him ran the Angel Wing. It had to be Silvio. There was no one like him.'

'Was he there all the time?'

He flew in and out and got them sorted with food and some got jobs. He was part of their survival.'

'So he must have his good side.'

Alan paused. 'I wouldn't like to say what it is. But good doesn't immediately come to mind.'

Eventually before Silvio started shooting 'Country Matters' in 1974 for which he won a BAFTA, I remembered to ask him about The Taft. He didn't know anything about it.

'Angel of the Gutter. Why deny it. All those good deeds.'

'I have never done a good deed in my life.'

'Yet you gave those people money. I was in the queue. Remember? Angel of the Gutter. You should put it on your gravestone.'

Silvio suddenly understood he was not afraid of dying. He saw it right there in that moment with those words.

'You gave those people food.'

He laughed drily. 'They were an inspiration. I don't do deeds good or otherwise. I took Pasolini there. He carried that image right into his films.'

'So they weren't deeds.'

'Just results.'

And I thought of all he'd done for the Kentish Town boys. Was that just results? Or because he liked being with them? Maybe he cared for them? I realised he kept his life simpler if he didn't have to give anything away. Was he good? Was he bad? Steve said it was the work that counts with Silvio.

CHAPTER 6

I DIDN'T REALISE AT FIRST that the disappearance of The Cat had something to do with the row I heard upstairs the night before. I could hear Luke's voice louder than the others. The row seemed to be concerning something said that needed an apology. Several times the front door was slammed as someone left. The boys rarely quarrelled. Then Luke left with the immortal words, 'Screw the skateboard!' I could definitely hear a female voice as a girl was escorted down the stairs and I opened my bedroom door. James closed it immediately. 'Nothing for you mum.' When the front door was slammed finally at 1.30 the walls shook as the neighbours battered their protest. They would report me to the council. The police. The local newspaper. Even the neighbours across the road had their say and then I recognised one. The actor Tom Bell leaning from a top window and his partner Frances Tempest the costume designer. I knew they were supposed to be in the area and there they were brought to their window by nocturnal mayhem and we became friends as deeply as the other lot became enemies.

The scriptwriter of Z Cars the popular TV series, who lived near the tube station, came round the next morning and said he had seen my son Tom rushing up the high street carrying a bunch of flowers. 'They weren't up to much but at least he'd paid for them. I usually see him sniffing glue.'

'Please don't tell me. I couldn't bear the things my son didn't do, leave alone what he did. So where is he going? The hospital?'

'To some girl. The others were mocking him. No wonder he felt a bit worse for it. But I'll say this for him. He stuck to his guns and rushed his way through the mob.'

It seemed according to my news sharer Rami that the previous night The Cat had got in with a skateboard she'd stolen, and becoming over cuddly with Luke, had pissed him off in front of the others. They teased Luke for being dominated by a girl especially with stolen goods. Who was he? PW or not? Tom objected to the accusation the skateboard was stolen. And then they turned on him and said he was in love with her and the fight broke out and The Cat was called a prostitute. Even Silvio could not sort it out. Gary the dealer threatened her with stuff he knew and she was sent off to spend the night in a doorway. And Tom was seen the next morning taking her flowers.

And then the gang was joined by other local boys who said he was a real wally for spending money on her. And they laughed and said he had wasted money on a tart. Pathetic. What did she know about flowers? Take her weeds. And Tom had said he did it because she felt terrible after what happened.

'What's it to you?'

'What happened last night makes her feel very bad. I know the feeling.' And with half the floral heads knocked off by the mocking group Tom carried on down the street.

'So you see why we don't have girls in our gang?' said Rami. Rami was the one to ask. Later I asked Tom who she was.

'Just a girl.'

'Do you like her?'

He said not especially. He just wanted to make her feel better after what had been said.

I said I was proud to be his mother. He'd done the right thing. I also knew he had a certain strength against the bad

34

things and that in turn worked out in my favour. He wasn't only the dope smoking glue sniffer. He could stand up for what he believed and could show love. He was his own person. I could go away and not worry about him. I got the ticket to New York.

*

Who was The Cat? I knew the little boy Rami was the one who would know. How did she get in the house? But also how did she get out? He said he never talked to her so I asked him why not. 'Because she's too–' He tried to find the words for 'grown up'. I thought Rami was 10, a runaway and had been saved from 'the meat rack' in Piccadilly. It got its name from the selling of young boys to paedophiles. That's how the story went. Rami who thought The Cat was too beautiful to talk to him said she had to go to work before midnight. I asked why. He said to bring back takeaways. She sold hotdogs on Kings Cross station. She wanted to save up to buy Luke a skateboard.

'Why?'

'Suppose she fancies him.' He was much more interested in telling me there was a ghost in the attic rooms.

'Yes and it's called Silvio.'

Rami was adamant. Those rooms were where the servants lived in the old days.

'So Silvio's teaching you history? So she makes money selling hotdogs?'

'To buy Luke a skateboard.' He nodded adamantly.

'Why pick on Luke. He is the one boy in that group that doesn't need money.'

There wasn't a lot of truth in any of it. I wanted to talk to her but where she had been she was no longer. Her presence was an illusion.

She stopped coming to the house and I didn't see her until months later and she was perhaps the most beautiful girl I had ever seen.

CHAPTER 7

I HAD WORKED FOR PIER Paulo Pasolini the Italian director on 'Canterbury Tales' in the early 1970s. I was asked to write a short interview for the London Magazine. Although he did not speak or understand much English he admired the literary content which his bilingual assistant translated for him. Several people of note had subscribed to this class magazine and I was fortunate to contribute a short story or article on several occasions. The editor Alan Ross published my first book 'A Lonely Diet' and with Francis Wyndham brought my writing to literary attention. They had previously rediscovered the writer Jean Rhys.

When I arrived in Canterbury on a cold afternoon there were some unfavourable top level discussions as the script's contents did not conform with what had been shown to and approved by the ecclesiastical authorities and it was suggested the location be moved to Hastings. I remembered it became quickly dark and cold as I waited in view of the renowned cathedral. While the tech crew speedily set up an interior scene filled with extras in 14th century good time attire, several log fires kept them warm. I found Pasolini precise, dry, intellectual and fervently political. I hadn't seen the funny side yet. The tech team not satisfied with the lighting asked for a delay to improve the broken stones and look of age. The cobbled entrance needed more paint to create shadow and suggest alleyways. The girls were ready to finally perform and the music was switched on. A last retouching of makeup and it became a Go scene. Pasolini had made some of the best films I had seen. 'Accattone', 'The Gospel according to St. Matthew', 'Theorem' with actors Terrence Stamp and Silvana Mangano. 'Oedipus Rex', which had such a strong effect on me I had to leave the cinema and get back my own reality. He could be too powerful but won all the awards.

Beyond the last moment Pasolini held up a hand. He had decided to quickly insert his arrival in Canterbury which he would now personally deliver in front of the gap of door, over fabricated and already falling to pieces. The light he said was exactly right for his scene. Spoken in Italian the short speech would be converted into English by the film's translator. It would take 10 minutes at most and then straight into the 14th century merriment and the smoking logs still giving their best. I was told there was not much time and I should give my questions in writing to the second assistant.

Was it my presence as an interviewer that persuaded Pasolini to say his lines in English. Assistants rushed to write the speech in large letters on a board above the door which in a rough wind began to creak.

The director had swiftly changed into his 14th C costume and the makeup team sped over his appearance with a brush and lifted his hair. He needed the words larger. After a quick rewrite he gave a shaky reading and decided he would do better sitting on a horse. Personally I was not partial to horses and it cut both ways. As part of the elite group by the creaking door I had to actually hold the strap while the director mounted the young and playful foal. The creature just needed one touch from me, one inhalation of my fearful sweat and its ears went back and its hind legs shot up and the director slid sideways.

I seemed to bring out a playful aggression in these animals. Maybe past life unfinished business? It certainly spiced up the present circumstances. Its eyes caught mine and resulted in a hideous neighing. Remembering the times I'd had to run for my life on such occasions I kept away behind the ailing door. The horse neighed playfully. It knew what it was doing and was put in its place by a slap on the nose from the script girl. The best thing to be said about her attitude was she was horsey. With overdone surprise she asked if I was alright, drawing the attention of the first assistant director mindful of cinematic payouts. He said I was not to touch any of the props or the personnel. 'Its only a horse,' and the script girl laughed. Its only a bull! Its a mere tarantula! The English could become simple-minded when it came to a horse. Pasolini asked for something better behaved. 'This animal is a bad dog.'

I let go of the door and suggested I move some distance away as I had on occasion a problem with horses. Untrue. On all occasions. Pasolini thought I was suggesting I sit on the horse myself and read the words above the door. By the time the confusion was sorted out and he on an older mare and the assistant holding the over large script at the right angle, it was too dark and the door still creaked.

'Let's go for it anyway,' said the first assistant with one eye on the worn out extras.

Pasolini peered forward in the dark and read the lines. 'I have finally from London arrived in Canterbury.'

'Cut!' shouted the assistant. 'Take 2. More light.'

The tech boys relit the scene quickly and brightened up the joyful extras behind the door where the fires dying left them cold. The hot drinks trailer was rushed in. Pasolini tried the lines several times but couldn't see the words. Then he had trouble with the pronunciation of Chaucer. It started to rain. I suggested he cut out the word 'finally'.

'And who are you?' Pasolini asked and straightened up on his horse.

'I am the writer from The London Magazine come to interview you. I've written and produced enough BBC Radio plays to know how one word can get stuck.'

Pasolini relieved suggested as I was a writer I should compose the two short lines of dialogue. More rain fell. We were offered umbrellas. Inside, the revellers were wrapped with blankets as the last log fire went out. I tried a sentence. I gave him my best.

'I have come from London and arrived in Canterbury.'

The first assistant said he would wrap the interior merriment scene before the extras froze to death.

'They have been valiant,' and Pasolini got off the horse and went in to thank them.

The horse left to its own devices rested its eyes on me. I took myself out of range. It gave a meaningful snort. The extras were taken by trailer to wardrobe. The scene would be shot the following day. Pasolini suggested one last try. It was suggested he too should give up his elusive scene until the following day.

No chance of that.

'Today I have come to Canterbury.' Perfect. Except he forgot 'today'. The assistants kicked out the smouldering log. Take 11. Forgot one word. Take 12. Forgot all the words.

He turned to me and suggested I get on the horse and say it for him.

'Never!'

He liked the way I shouted never and wanted it introduced into his speech.

Quickly I responded.

'Never did I think I would reach this day. I have arrived in Canterbury.'

The crew actually applauded and congratulated me. What they were really saying was, get the hell out! Pasolini was as soaked as the horse. The last extras insisted in getting into their outer clothes. The dining car was going to shut. The authorities wanted to move the set to Hastings. Now.

Beyond reason Pasolini spoke. 'I have arrived at last in

Canterbury. Never will I do this again.' And the horse rose onto its back feet and the scene was done.

It took longer than many in a big epic. It had taken one and a quarter hours.

It was nicknamed 'Gone with the wind'. All it needed was Silvio.

*

After a light dinner in Canterbury Pasolini decided we should all get in the car and go to London. No-one was tired. I wasn't sure if it was to go to a club or for him to see a friend. He had spent a wonderful time describing how he set up scenes to film and how he used certain aspects of an actor's face or expression repeatedly as I would use a noun or verb in my writing. I understood when he described Silvana Mangano why he brought that face so much into frame and why he used so often what she gave him. Talking together with his personal translator was unforgettable.

We crowded into the car and he asked how long it would take. It seemed we were going for my sake, to take me home safely. He felt we had more to talk about and could spend these short hours well. I was impressed and honoured but said I would take a local hotel.

'All full,' said the first assistant.

Not long after leaving Canterbury we passed a young man standing by the road seemingly hitch-hiking. In spite of the weather he wore a white shirt and a jacket lay across his bag. He looked attractive and well made. Pasolini told the driver to slow down and turned to get a better look at him. 'Stop!' he said and the car slithered to a halt and the guy ran forward. Yes he was well put together with a certain wildness and physicality the director liked. He was a Scot from rough Glasgow and wanted to get to London urgently. Pasolini liked everything about him. He even had a certain danger. The interpreter asked what we should call him.

'Scot will do!' the boy told us. 'You don't need to know more.'

Pasolini was pleased. You never know where good things are coming from.

'Let's put him in the film.' Even the translator looked surprised.

'A star is born,' the translator said and the car spun around and we returned to Canterbury.

The bilingual interpreter gave me his room and said to join them for a drink.

Scot after a few beers opened up and seemed to be involved in gang warfare.

'Because of football?' asked the interpreter. 'Celtic vs Rangers up in Glasgow. You support the wrong side.'

'Because of murder.'

'They won't find you here,' I told him.

'They'll find me. Don't worry about that.' I could see Pasolini liked watching him. He was watchable. He was offered a small role in the film the next morning.

Yes the director was certainly cheered up by this street boy from Badlands. For some reason the whole thing made me think about Silvio. It was the kind of thing he would understand. But not do. He wouldn't trust his love of the unknown to operate in his work. Remembering he was also Italian I mentioned him to Pasolini, taking a chance, and his eyes brightened and he was full of words, memories, laughter. He recounted a story where he was trapped in a lift in New York and how these Italians laughed. Silvio was in some extraordinary happening and getting away with it. I would never know what Silvio had done that had so thrilled the dry intellectual, anti-fascist director because no-one translated the story. It went too fast and needed the speed and to recount it afterwards was to kill the joy. And it was personal. Later Pasolini said he had written a poem about Silvio. It had been composed after they had shared the lift experience. I did try to ask the interpreter something of the story but he had to deal with the unexpected boy from Glasgow.

'Early start everyone.'

*

Pasolini fitted Scot into a small scene where he would jump down from a ledge into a kitchen and ask his mother to get him some food. Scot could choose the way he spoke to her and even the words that he would normally use. With each scene the words got more inappropriate. It didn't take as long as the horse but Scot couldn't remember what he was asking for. 'You don't ask for fucking food where I come from. You take it.'

He had to push through a gap in the wall which represented a medieval window and jump down into the stone kitchen. And the sun had to be behind him. It became clear the gap between a trained actor and a simple passer-by with a few lines to deliver. After take 10 the sun had moved and they had to light artificially. Scot couldn't remember his line or what he was doing and after the sixth jump from the ledge he became clumsy, his ankle damaged and the actress playing the mother started cracking up. Pasolini seemed okay and then the legal crew arrived to move the whole lot to Hastings. And catching sight of Scot they thought it should be quick. Scot jumped and froze. The interpreter suggested he hurry up with his one line. 'Ask your mother for anything,' he suggested. Scot turned on him.

'Do you have trouble?' the interpreter asked.

'Yes I don't have a fucking mother.'

He asked me to join him behind the coffee trailer. He needed to get out of sight.

'I am not into this stuff. I'm no actor.'

'Yes. Got that.'

'I wasn't on the road last night for kicks. I have to get to London. I'm blamed for what happened in Glasgow last week. It doesn't look good. And the Celtic gang in my face.' He lowered his voice. 'It's not them. It's a gang from Glasgow that have betrayed them. And then if they find out I have done a film for god's sake and made some brass they will finish me off. It's no film story up there I can tell you.'

'Tell the director. He will help. He will understand.'

'To be honest with you I don't know who is who and what they're doing. And I've screwed up my ankle. Could you help me get out of here. That Italian guy! I can't make him out. I've got to get to Croydon. I need a car and some cash.'

The first assistant found us. 'Get a move on folks. Last take.' To me he said, 'There's been some queries about Boyfriend. Police and others.' He got hold of Scot and helped him up onto the ledge. 'We've covered the floor with blankets so trust to jump down.' And this to a boy who had never trusted anything.

But he took the last leap into pain and the take was ruined by a terrible noise as dozens of Scots guys ran towards us over the hill. Screw stardom. They wanted to get the little shit and kill him.

The only person not concerned was Pasolini. He ordered the cameras to keep going and got it all on film and loved it.

CHAPTER 8

'IT ISN'T HALF GOING AT a speed,' said James. 'It's all this attention. You want to cover it up with a cloth. Don't want to wear it out. It's the school's pet.' The dogs sat on the chairs and cats on other surfaces glued to the spectacle of the hamster on its wheel. Tom had brought it back from school to show the headmaster he was reliable.

When I came back with a cover the first thing I noticed were the dogs hiding under the table. They had the same look as when they had stolen a bag of croissants from the cupboard. The cats were not to be seen. Just one tail hanging from up the chimney of the fireplace. And then I noticed the wheel was not spinning. And then I noticed the hamster lying on its side on the bottom of the cage.

'Oh bad,' said James reaching into the cage. 'It might just be worn out so call the vet. Tom can't go back to school without it.'

The vet's wife said her husband wasn't expected until later. She had the plummy tones of someone who made too much money. I asked her to get hold of the vet immediately. I had spent enough on him for a bit of service. She asked what was the problem and I suddenly felt quite sad myself. James had wrapped the little creature in cotton wool.

'Of course I'll get my husband if it's an emergency. Is it a dog? Or a horse?'

I could tell that was all she dealt with.

'It's a hamster.'

'A – hamster!' She burst out laughing. It was terrible.

'My son loves that pet. How dare you.' I hung up. James came back from the pet shop in the alley. 'It's the best I can do.' It was nothing like the original. It was a rodent, dark looking, dusty with a long scar down the side of its face. 'I called it Boadicea.'

James looked at it hopefully. 'I don't think it will quite do it mum. I mean it won't fool Tom.'

The vet rang and remembered I was not a big client but the bread and butter kind. He apologised for his wife and said she had laughed because she was shocked. His voice was too steady as though determined not to laugh. What was it about hamsters? 'She had a shock because normally we treat large animals especially horses.' He got over himself and suggested revival techniques way far too late.

We drank a bit that night and forgetting about Boadicea I put my bare foot on its cage. She bit deep into my toe. I did not know hamsters could bite flesh. At hospital they gave me a shot and stitches.

When I got home the hamster was looking at me from the front of its cage as it fell sideways immobile.

'Oh no it can't be.'

Boadicea was dead.

'It must have been all the alcohol you've drunk that killed it,' said Luke.

'Maybe they can't take drink.'

'Coming from that school I doubt it.' Whatever killed it the cage was empty.

Rami said, 'replacements are never the answer.'

CHAPTER 9

I NEVER SAW SILVIO BROKE. I saw Silvio saying he was broke.
I was walking the dogs up Highgate Road to the Heath when he
came towards me. He'd been away several weeks in India setting
up his film based on the classic book, 'Staying On'. He looked
thinner as though he'd been through demanding times. Actually
I wasn't sure this light stepping person was even him but surely
Silvio would not be like anyone else. Whatever his state he
always looked as though he could handle the present situation.
Gloria the third dog growled. That was enough identification.

'I need money,' he said.

'Why?'

'I'm broke. Let's go and see Harry Alan Towers.'
Thoughtlessly he put out a hand to slap or stroke the unfriendly
dog. I recommended he keep his hands to himself. I told him he
looked thinner. Different.

'I wasn't going to eat off the street stalls. Some of the actors
did that to slim. I saw it as a test I didn't need. So I went on
a fast.' He patted his fleshless stomach and managed a proud
smile.

He looked across the road at the wet fish shop and asked if
I had any money. Could I buy him a mackerel and grill it with

potatoes and mushrooms. 'I'll make it worth your while.'

'God what does that mean?'

'A script job with Harry. I'll cut you in for a first draft. Let's go and see him.' He took the dogs' leads. Another mistake. Gloria snapped in warning and he ignored the pain and crossed to the pub. 'We leave them here and get a taxi.' He pushed the pub door and Gloria didn't like whatever she made of this change of plan. He decided to phone the boys to come and get the dogs from the pub.

'Get that one out of here!' The pub owner was no fan of Gloria.

I took back control of the leads. 'The dogs come with us. I have to talk to my agent.'

'It's not your agent that's going to get this job for you. It's me.'

Miranda Stewart-Cobb, and in spite of her snobbish attitudes was a good friend of mine, passed on the way to buy some fish. She recognised Silvio, which made her stop and find out how well I was doing or not. For once he was not playful and she saw her fish purchase a better option.

'She's got money,' I told him. 'But most of it in the bank.'

'She's put her whole life in the bank.' He sighed. And then he looked at me and laughed, suddenly pleased. 'I'm glad you are still here.'

'Likewise.' I wasn't sure about the 'here'.

'Come to India next month. You'll like Simla in the mountains. Somehow those things don't matter up there.'

It wasn't clear what things. He got a taxi and we took the dogs home and then south to smart Fitzrovia.

Harry Alan Towers was someone Silvio went to for money. He had produced an assortment of films, TV and radio. He had done remakes that had made him rich. And soft porn richer. He'd worked with some good actors including Orson Welles.

'We could have Dennis in this movie and that would pay your food bills.'

Silvio probably thought that sounded helpful.

'Dennis as in Hopper?' I knew better than to get into that.

The taxi stopped by a classy Georgian three-storey block of flats still retaining their charm. 'Virginia Woolf was here. Still is. Harry's good with ghosts.'

I waited for him to pay the cab. He pulled out both trouser pockets. Empty. He started to get out and then turned round. 'Give him a tip.' And he walked to the apartment entrance. Then he decided he liked the railings. 'Not been touched since Second World War.'

I paid the taxi and joined him at the door. 'Broke means you still pay taxis.'

'Oh stop it. You know you're going to get a deal.' Again he rang the bell and spoke into the answer-phone. 'Play time's over Harry. I'm back so forget that siesta. I've got a project.' Without lowering his voice he turned to me and said, 'Harry's got a girlfriend with sensational breasts. If it's that one in the bedroom we might as well go and see a movie.'

The buzzer and a man's voice. We were told to meet in the library. It was a harmonious place. Real money. I asked who owned it. 'Harry of course.'

'The whole building?'

'He has whole buildings. No need to be impressed. He's also got a smart voice. If you like those you'll notice a touch of common vowels. He went to the right public school but they could never quite wipe out the past. Traders in fish.'

The maid took us to the library and said Mr Harry was on a call.

'Tell him to get all that bed stuff over with and he gets first offer. And I've got something for Dennis.' Silvio accepted the offer of coffee gracefully. He mostly had good manners.

The moment the maid left, Silvio sped along the corridor into a closed office. I followed. The desk was piled with scripts and documents. Silvio fell to the floor and lay spread out on his stomach. I dropped down beside him and thought he could be unconscious. I asked the expected questions. Then his hands reached the rubbish bin and pulled it toward him and sat up.

'God you gave me a fright. I though it was a heart attack. What's the matter with you.' Now I was angry.

He was picking at the rubbish and straightening out crumpled papers. A brief look at one, and he tossed them to one side.

'What the hell are you looking for, all his business stuff is on his desk.'

'No good looking there. That's for show.' He found a document he liked and reached further until his head was under the desk. He straightened out a receipt and was pleased. 'This is better. One hundred thousand came in today. You can never tell how much someone has. He'll tell you this and that. He never has enough. He's got enough on this other document to fund the whole film.'

'What the hell!' Harry was in the room.

Silvio slithered back from under the table and stood up holding the valuable documents. Harry gave them a mere glance then sat at his desk hair on end. Silvio kicked through the scattered papers on the floor and picked up another one. 'You want to be careful what you throw away. You never know who can get in here. Harry your waste bin is your money box.'

Harry was early 60s and looked as though he had been in the army. He had many diversions and could afford them. He went to the right clubs and as Silvio remarked had three quarters the right voice. He didn't look seedy. I thought Silvio had overloaded the description. I thought here was a man who got what he wanted.

'You've come to the right place but at the wrong time,' said Harry. 'I've just paid the service charges.'

'Here's some good news.' And Silvio flattened out the second smaller document. 'Came in at 3 o'clock today. I bet you forgot all about it.'

Silvio indicated I sit down on a sofa and he pulled a chair up to the desk. Silvio bent down and reached into the rubbish. He came up with a rejected postcard of a naked model. He showed it to Harry, 'I don't know what she did wrong to end in the bin but she's just right.'

'She's from the 40s.' Harry moved things on his desk. Nothing was as it seemed.

'Exactly. The 40s.'

'And here's more good news. You'll get Dennis. And he's off the sauce.'

'What does he play these days?'

'Whatever you want him to be. The husband? A lover? A soldier come through the window at night?'

'Reliable?'

'He's coming along nicely. He's doing his program. I've got him on my next Spanish film. 'The sky is falling'. Win has written it.' They stared at each other across the desk and Silvio whispered 'Eva Peron'.

'Out of the question.'

'But you've just found out you're a rich and lucky man Harry.'

Harry stood up. 'Can't do more than 70.'

Silvio pretended to laugh.

'No exteriors.'

'We don't need them. It's low budget as hell. Patrice gets very real on low budget. It's how she lives.'

'Thank you!!' I said.

'Not spending that money,' said Harry.

'The inside story Harry. Of Eva Peron. Inside. In this case it means not outside where expenses begin. We are drawn into the grey solitude of her bedroom. Why is she sitting all alone like a child on the side of her bed. What has happened to her? The rows of furs, the endless boxes of shoes, the rails of silks. What has she done?' He turns to me. 'Patrice is at her best on this stuff.' I had a bad few minutes wondering what that was.

'She's gone further than she could. How far could Eva Peron

51

go.' He paused so Harry could get mindful of what going further could mean.

'Can't do more than TV.'

Silvio sighed. 'I've just been crawling on your floor and find 10 times that. You are richer than you think and now you start to play dumb.' Harry started towards the door. 'Where's it being shot?'

'South America.'

'There's something missing here that I can't afford. The Peron regime had soldiers and loads of them. Thousands. They are never low budget.' He went to open the door.

'Harry there are half a million. But they're all outside. You hear them. Remember sound? You don't see them. Maybe a couple by the door. Let's do a lineup of nice new actresses. We need an unknown beauty. And get your mind off all this palace expense.'

'Palace?' Harry looked genuinely surprised.

'Well she's got to live somewhere. Same as always. You get 70%, I take 10 and we make the winner of the year.'

Harry turned to me. 'No soldiers.'

Out in the street Silvio paid me 200 pounds and put 10 times that into his shirt pocket.

'Now you can afford to cook us a good fish dinner.'

CHAPTER 10

IVAN MOFFAT THE CELEBRATED SCREENWRITER and socialite approached the pool with a studied sense of purpose and did the required 6 lengths followed with a spontaneous display of butterfly strokes meant to be playful.

It was superb morning, the light touched by the Hollywood magician that looked after the stars on the top of the hill and kept the smog way down with the losers. Ivan saw me standing in the shade of the doorway. He laughed, 'You look like the little match girl. Come on! Jump in!'

I said I didn't have a swimsuit. I didn't have anything needed to recover from the ravages of the night before. I had to spend serious time on my appearance after that extreme flight to LA. I knew better than to ask if he had a hairdryer.

'Don't worry about a swimsuit. There's no one around here. Just take off your clothes.'

I did manage the t-shirt. I wasn't worried about what came off but what scuttled towards the corner of the pool. It looked like a spider. It could not be a spider. It was a bad visual moment left over from the journey of the night before.

'What's wrong with you?' Ivan asked, all attempts at hospitality gone.

I couldn't say I just saw a spider. This was Hollywood. I took off my jeans. Ivan, and they didn't call him 'the finder of perfect things' for nothing, sighed loudly. He wasn't afraid to recognise perfection. 'Jeans went out at 17. And that fabric is only to be worn if you are making a point of it and you are not.'

I approached the pool. The creature had been too large to be a spider and I thought I could hear a rustling in the undergrowth. Did Ivan unexpectedly have a pet? I was to find out the hard way.

'Why are you keeping them on?' He pointed to my underclothes. Eventually naked I pressed a foot into the water. It was rainwater and here and there a twig had fallen, bracken floated. It was heavy water, natural, and no chlorine here. I heard a voice I surely recognised. Jack Nicholson said, 'Not bad for your age.'

I had never met him but could not fault that voice.

Ivan looked at me and asked what was the matter with me. He dreaded guests especially sick ones. I was seeing things. Now hearing them. I blamed it on the flight.

He couldn't scoff enough. 'It's always a bit turbulent crossing the Rockies.'

'A bit? The plane dropped 21,000 feet.'

'I doubt it. It's CAT, clear air turbulence. It's not the plane. It's the sky. God lives in the sky. Didn't you tell me that. So you are looked after whatever happens.' He held out a hand. Would I accept the touch of an atheist. I still didn't get into the pool. I knew I was becoming a disappointment as his guest but spoke anyway. 'I also heard a voice.'

He didn't reply. Then he sighed. 'It's only Jack.'

I turned slowly prepared to see anything after the spider. Jack Nicholson leaned over the hedge grinning. 'You're not bad for your age.' He leaned over to look approvingly at my legs.

'Not bad for any age,' said Ivan.

Jack laughed. 'I meant you. We can see her attributes and don't need to mention them!' The grin stretched to the familiar

Jack smile as he watched me undecided quivering at the edge. The black spider thing had scuttled to the pool and was probably in it. Also swimming was not my thing.

'You have been blessed with that body.' Jack sounded full of praise.

Me or my host? The movie star's eyes were playful as they rested on my body. The only thing was to jump into the water and get it over with.

'That body will carry you well into old age.'

Confused now I wondered how old I did look.

Then Ivan said, 'And I take care of it. 10 lengths every morning.'

'I saw only 6,' said Jack.

'And no drinks before 6 pm.'

Ivan stood up in the water and pulled my head towards his. I thought he was going to kiss me. He murmered against my ear. 'He's trying to bait me with all these little half good, half bad comments. He's after something. Don't concern yourself.'

What could a global superstar want from Ivan?

'You are so right,' said Jack, still some distance away. 'Don't bother with all that whispering. I don't miss much.'

'That you don't.' Ivan agreed.

'Will you be in my new movie?'

'Which is?'

'The Two Jakes.'

'God no.' And Ivan dived deep under the water and stayed out of sight.

'Not the usual reaction to a movie offer.' Jack still smiled.

'Maybe he is overwhelmed.' The best I could come up with.

'You don't see many pools like this in Hollywood.' Jack spoke thoughtfully and his voice still carried across the garden. 'This is the real thing. Deep water, a natural temperature, Ivan doesn't use all that disinfectant stuff that kills anything. Look at the shrubs. They are alive and there are wild flowers. Most pools in this town are no more than garden decorations, fit for those artificial gnomes that are said to bring bad luck. But then Ivan is real.'

What was one of the biggest stars in the world standing for several minutes looking over a hedge and assessing the neighbour's ordinary swimming pool.

'I like it here because I am just here. I don't have to 'be' anything. For once.' I thought I should come up with a reply but couldn't think of anything. 'Why don't you swim?' His suggestion sounded delicious, inviting.

'I don't swim normally.' I was so overwhelmed I could only tell the truth.

'I'd love to see abnormal swimming. Give it a go.'

Ivan came up for air.

'You can play yourself,' Jack told him. 'I would just love to have that exceptional voice and high class manner. You have all the charm you need. It's perfect for the movie.'

'I don't do masquerades.'

'What a shame,' said Jack.

Ivan handed me a towel. 'You had better have some breakfast.'

'I'd like that,' said Jack. 'Do I need to dress?'

And Jack left the hedge and pulled himself over the gate. I did try a length or two. Crawl was my safest. And then I met a large black object with eyes at the corner of the pool. It was no garden gnome. For a moment it did look like a spider. It scuttled onto a long waterlogged plant towards me. It was a spider. I screamed. Ivan said I had cramp. I could only point.

'Yeah, a challenging arrival for you,' said Jack. 'Having to stay afloat and look into the eyes of a substantial spider. Let's hope it's not Australian. They don't mess about.'

'Oh don't be ridiculous.' It turned out Ivan liked spiders and had no time for people's fear. 'Pancakes for you Jack? Lemon or maple syrup? The usual egg and bacon?'

'Anything as long as I end up looking like you. If I get to that age that is.'

He got me out of the water and wrapped a towel around my shoulders. He was smaller than I expected and wore a cap low over his eyes. I wasn't even sure this was Jack. Putting his arm around me we went to Ivan's bedroom and he gave me a mineral water with lemon. His voice was soothing as he told me I had had a horror start. 'That captain deserves a hell of a thank you. He's a hero.' He crouched beside me. 'Do you want to talk about it?'

'It felt like this is it.' He encouraged me into a chair and asked if I wanted to shower now or after breakfast. I wanted to stay with him no matter how unhealthily drowned I was. He helped me dry my hair. He was kind and I didn't expect that from a global celebrity. Maybe this was his look-a-like stand-in. I could hear Ivan taking a brief shower. Jack kept his arm around me as he said he knew all about the plane.

'It sure dropped. It's made the news.'

'Captain Bear. He was talking to us all the time reassuring us as he got us through it. I remember people screaming.' Suddenly I said, 'Have you got a tranquilliser?'

'Sure thing.' He put his hand in his vest pocket and took out a small box of capsules. 'You never know who's going to need one!' Then he laughed. 'Even me.' He poured me more mineral water.

I just held it like a holy bead. 'Yes he was called Captain Bear.'

'Even the name sounds reassuring. It was a spectacular drop. No wonder you need some care.'

'And then we came into land and there were the ambulances and fire crew. And the captain got a huge applause which just didn't stop. A lot of people crying.'

'I'm tearful myself. A great guy. Don't let Ivan get his own way with it. He doesn't see it. I suppose because he's been in the war. Then you get over that to look into the eyes of a sizeable spider.'

'Are there many around here?' I asked.

He paused. No sound of water. Ivan was in the kitchen. Sizzle sounds of frying bacon. 'I will ask the pool man. He looks after Ivan's drainage. It's a Roger Corman horror film. I used to work for him. I used to write this stuff. But don't tear up your return ticket and start taking boats and trains. Maureen Stapleton the actress had a terrible landing in LA so tore up her return ticket. And went back on Amtrak to New York and got on the boat for England. Halfway out in the ocean it caught fire.' He paused and almost laughed. 'Then they had to airlift the passengers back to New York. And back she went on the train to LA.' He held my hand and asked if I wanted to see his shrink. 'If I've still got one. Because I'm never too sure in that department.'

'No she does not. Wish to see someone's shrink.'

Ivan was in the room.

'She's English. Breakfast ready.'

*

Breakfast was relaxed and the food well prepared. Ivan suddenly stared at the plates. 'I love the yellow of butter. It's one of the many things I remember about France. That rich yellow. And bread fresh from the market.'

'You were there in the war,' Jack told him.

'And afterwards. On the last day of that war I got shot by a sniper in Paris. It got me in the knee. I was one of the very last to be hit. Took some time in the hospital to get it mended.'

I could see Jack liked that story even though he already knew it. And of course Ivan still walked with a limp.

'That's why you write such damn good war films.' Jack gave me half of the last pancake and asked what I was doing in LA.

I had three books under offer with producers which in most people's opinion sounded good but not at this breakfast table. Answering for me Ivan said I was doing a film with Silvio Narizzano. Later he told me it sounded better than the three possibles. He obviously didn't know Silvio.

'I've heard of him,' said Jack.

"Georgy Girl',' Ivan said quickly. 'You've heard of that.' Jack said he had. 'It grossed more than any film in the UK for years. And elsewhere. Then 'Jaws' came along.'

Jack gave me a provocative smile. 'Well at least we've stopped him from talking about spiders.'

So Ivan started talking about spiders. There was no need to demonise them.

And they did good for the planet. And they were clever creatures.

Jack didn't quite get that. 'They can nip or is it sting? They can kill us.' He opened his arms wide. 'They make lousy pets. What's the point of these silent scary looking rodents creeping about on all those eight legs.'

'They have six legs,' Ivan corrected him. 'They are not rodents. They are beautifully made.'

'My god.' Jack mopped his head and looked at me. 'Have you stayed here before?'

'I've visited mostly. Several times. We know each other from London.'

'Well I hope you do a good film with Silvio Narizzano. Where are you shooting?'

'Nicaragua,' said Ivan.

'But there's a war there.'

'Exactly,' said Ivan. 'He likes it on the edge.' So he did know Silvio.

Later when I asked him why he'd chosen Nicaragua he said it just got one's mind off even worse outcomes of that film story.

Jack stood up. 'I didn't get much sleep. Those motorbikes again on Mulholland.'

'It's McQueen,' said Ivan. 'It's better to ignore him.'

'We can't do that. He'll miss the attention. Let's tell him he's great on a bike but it's killing our sleep. Then he'll stop.'

Ivan said it had no chance of working.

'The Big One is back now. He'll have something to say.'

'He'll tell us we are getting old and he'll go out and join them,' said Ivan.

'He's heavy again.' Jack was thoughtful. 'You'll have to start getting his favourite provisions in and fill your cupboards. By the way, you called her the little match girl. Wasn't she from the 18th century?'

'I think you mean the 1800s,' said Ivan.

'I flunked history,' said Jack.

'But you've got good hearing,' said Ivan. 'That must've carried right across the pool.'

'I don't need things carried. I've still got my hearing.'

Jack had enjoyed the breakfast and allowed the atmosphere to be light.

Now it was time to make his offer. 'You get to play yourself in 'The Two Jakes'. A 30 day shoot for you and right here in town. We start next year. It's a follow up from 'China Town', need I say more? Say your price.'

'No to the movie.'

Jack sat down again and smiled. It took care of the tension. It was a substantial smile even for him.

'You know you could even write the script. Robert's producing so we have all the money.'

Ivan asked him why he always smiled. Jack replied immediately. 'Because I like what I see.'

'Animals show their teeth in aggression to defend themselves.'

'That's great for them. Thank god spiders don't smile.'

Ivan stood up. 'I'm not an actor.'

'Everyone's an actor. It's such a waste. That English voice. Classy and damned attractive. Not afraid to be old style.'

'But I'm not English.'

'You were a minute ago. What happened?'

'I was born in Cuba and my father Curtis Moffat, the photographer, was American.'

'So you're just one of us.'

Ivan reached out and touched his shoulder. 'Backgammon at 6?'

'Sure.'

And to me he said, 'How long are you here for?'

Ivan said that no guest ever stayed over two days. He, the host got bored and so did they.

Jack started for the door. 'So, it's no, but I know where to come if I need some 'not normal' swimming.'

He was no stand-in. This was Jack Nicholson. He left by the formal exit.

'He took it well,' I said to be positive.

'No,' said Ivan immediately.

'He gave you a good smile.'

'He wasn't smiling inside.'

*

Ivan's shopping was frugal. He liked to go to the market during its quiet time and spend the rest of the day writing unless he had a lunch. He knew where to buy the best bread and croissants. The fruit juice he prepared himself. 'You need to keep in good shape.' He removed the chocolate bar I'd just chosen and put it back on the pile. He reconsidered that for a mere moment and put it back in the basket and added another two bars. Had he gone mad? This was the kind of extravagance he dreaded. Other attractive items were added and the basket was overfull. I told him I didn't know he liked this kind of food and he didn't answer.

On the way back he bought nuts and raisins, enough for a family. I thought I'd better shut up. Maybe he was a secret middle of the night eater. Now I thought about it he wasn't just a social figure out on the town. He was also a loner. He could spend days without seeing anyone. Was that when the comfort eating took place.

*

I wasn't invited to play that night but only watch. Ivan told me I was a bad player because I enjoyed the game and wanted to win and did not listen to him. I did not know when to become cautious. He would say, 'I would not make that move honey.' I made it because everything inside me was for it and would lead to my victory over him. He'd sigh and roll the dice and throw a couple of sixes and that was me out. I asked him why he won all the time.

'Out of 20 games with you I will win 19 and you 1. It's partly dice luck but mostly skill.' He played all over the world and was invited to represent clubs and businesses. They backed him and he brought back the crown. Was this why the elite of Hollywood came to his 6 pm backgammon games. There were three tables set up and I didn't know if Jack actually played or was interested in the action.

'How does he do it?' he asked. And then he suddenly got up and left as his favourite team the Lakers were playing.

Yes he was angry. Maybe.

Later that night Ivan told me the reason he would not do Jack's film. 'It's a coke film and you end up with two holes for nostrils and no bone in your nose. It's going to be a drugged disaster. It won't work. I don't know what Robert Towne is thinking of?'

He was a well established writer and scripted 'China Town'. Robert Evans was the producer and was scheduled to start shooting in 1984 but didn't get it made until 1990. By then it had been through many kinds of adversity.

Now Ivan said how much money was made out of drugs in Hollywood. He poured an early whiskey in defiance. 'It is said Robert Evans spends thousands a week on cocaine. He runs the studio. He is bright, intelligent, chooses wonderful subjects to film and he gets a collapsed nose.'

So Ivan didn't put himself into a project he could sense would not work no matter who the stars or how big the payoff. Anyway he was now scripting the 'The Thorn Birds', a best selling Australian novel and the adaptation was rumoured to be exceptionally well paid. Another factor apart from the distorted nose was he didn't need the money.

Marlon Brando, Ivan Moffat and Jack Nicholson lived at the top of Mulholland and Coldwater. They were close neighbours. Further down this charmed hill Christopher Isherwood had a house and across from him the painter David Hockney. They didn't meet often as one or the other was usually away and they had their own lives but Marlon certainly visited Ivan and by a surprising route.

*

Ivan Moffat was legendary. As Jack Nicholson said, the 'Real Thing'. He'd had a remarkable career and was commonly said to be on top of his game. He had worked with the brilliant director George Stevens in the 40s and 50s on 'Shane', 'A Place in the Sun' and 'Giant' for which Ivan's script was nominated for an Oscar. He had scripted 'Tender is the Night' and 'The Great Escape' for which he would not take a credit. Also John Frankenheimer's 'Black Sunday', and the war films included 'The Heroes of Telemark' with Kirk Douglas.

He was sought after socially and seemed to know or know of every exceptional or famous person in the world. Effortlessly he knew them and in turn they recognised him.

Was it his part in the anti-fascist battle of Cable Street in London's East End in 1936 in which he participated and filmed the drama that started his career. I understood George Stevens was there or certainly helped with the film. As the British fascists' leader Sir Oswald Mosley marched 5000 of his uniformed men, thousands turned out to show they had no use for fascism. Ivan felt deeply about politics and no matter what was happening in his own life he followed and supported eloquently the fight against fascism. Maybe it was this integrity that attracted people to him in an unstable world.

Married twice he had affairs and partnerships throughout

his life and some of these women never got over him and others never forgot him. My mother in law Oona Chaplin called him an Homme Fatale. The movie stars too including Liz Taylor.

He was also a world class backgammon champion.

CHAPTER 11

THE FIRST TIME I WENT to Jack's place he was watching television and although the room was hardly lit he was wearing his shades. He said he could no longer go out. Although it was his favourite team playing he seemed withdrawn. I didn't remember much about the room except there was an old style olive coloured fridge in one corner. A man was sitting at the end of the table. He was effortlessly upright and unmoving on the stiff chair, no doubt through spending many hours on physical training. Although the room was dark he exuded his own brand of darkness, so black, so intense, it almost became liquid as ink or paint. The liquid shadows kept him in darkness so what he was I could not tell. I thought part of his covering was an old style mackintosh from the 1940s covered with gleaming puddles, an emergency coat no longer in this world. His eyes unmoving stayed on mine. Jack had said a name when I first came in but the man had not moved or spoken. I thought it was Elmer.

He was a scientific experiment only possible in Hollywood. His darkness was taken to its furthest extreme so it turned into thick liquid before it made its next transformation. He was truly still as though made of stone. This figure belonged in a graveyard. He stayed motionless not to disturb the process.

His white face, surely chalk became the headstone and words appearing just above its top. Stillness, no movement ever, no sound, no sorrow, death. The hair was grizzled close to the skull and didn't look real either. Then I thought it was the darkness that gave him these sinister aspects and I should see him in sunlight and all this would make sense. He probably had an enviable poolside body and delicate tan.

I started to get up as I needed to go to the brightness of the kitchen where Tim, the young Cordon Bleu chef was cooking dinner. The sounds of stirring and chopping were reassuring. And then I remembered when I came into the room I had encountered a strong smell familiar in Kentish Town. Sinsemella weed? I was breathing it in and probably high as you get. So I needed to steady up before thinking too much about oddness. He was probably a normal guy in a suit.

Jack turned and saw us stranded. 'Why don't you tell Robert about the spiders?'

Yes of course. That's what he was. A rodent exterminator. Then he moved. Nothing much but coming out of that stillness I was shocked. He scratched one arm. And then the words above him were clear. 'Thorn Birds'.

'One spider,' I corrected Jack. And then Kentish Town saved me. Of course I knew the smell when I came into the room and knew from the past it was too heavy for me. The kids puffed it as though their lives depended on it. Jack's variety had a few extras.

Even Jack seemed withdrawn. The Lakers didn't please him. He got up.

'Even they can't do it for me. What's the matter with them?'

He gave me a knowing look. Had I been freely partaking of the drug? 'You don't get this stuff in London,' he said. 'It's straight from South America.'

I told him I didn't smoke it.

'Ah so you'd like a little snort. Why didn't you say.'

'I don't do drugs.'

'Christ!' he said. Then he paused. 'Is this the Moffat at

work. Don't listen to him and we won't tell him.' He poured me a large drink.

'She doesn't do that either,' said the tombstone. 'No gear. No alcohol. What does she do? It must be Charlie.'

'I'm on another track.'

'I wonder just what that would be?' said the tombstone. 'I bet it's TM.'

He was now scratching his side. Just once. A pause. Then a dozen scratches. And now he was restless in his chair. The scratching became shaking but Jack took no notice. I supposed he was used to it. Tombstone was right about the TM.

Then this person spoke again and his voice got to the point. He was used to getting his meaning across. The voice and communication quite different from all the chemical reaction to his life and drugs.

'How well do you know Moffat?' he asked as though it was a legal matter. I said I was a friend. He asked Jack for another glass and called him Johnny. 'Give her a sparkling water.'

'This project Moffat's on now, 'The Thorn Birds', is not going to work.' His face was still ashen. He was coming down from a fix, Jack said later.

'The director is going to walk and it won't be a movie. It will be a TV movie or a series.'

'So what can I do about it?'

'You're a friend. He will have his work cut out to get another commission.'

I asked why.

'His style of film is yesterday. You can only have so many 'The Last 10 Days of Hitler' and then he'll be too old.' He continued predicting bad futures. I was about to get one.

'Ivan should take what's on the table and play it clever. There's money and there is money. The sort he thinks he's got is–'

'A duck's ass,' said Jack.

'So what about you?' the new advisor asked.

Forgetting what Ivan had told me I mentioned the three

options. I added 'Siesta' in which Polanski had shown an interest.

'Never! You'll never get past the guy who opens the studio door. And Polanski is not without his problems. I know he thinks he's dealing with Ivan on a project about cannibals. Forget it. Impossible. After Sharon Tate died.'

So I told him about the Modigliani book due for publication. He didn't let me finish.

'You won't get your pitch past the first 'M' in the artist's name. Won't go in Texas.'

Was it the drugs or was I suddenly a glutten for put down but I added Lauren Bacall had optioned one of the three books on offer.

Even Jack laughed. The new enemy shrugged. 'Who's your agent?'

'Robbie Lanz.' That was big talk. I was with his assistant.

'Does he still talk with that mid European accent he's kept for 20 years?' His imitation was funny. At least Jack thought so. He didn't like me. I knew that.

'You need to have legs in this town or you'll be gone in the first breeze from Malibu. They'll say Where's Patrice? And after a month it will be Who's Patrice?'

I came from Kentish Town. I was glad. It had given me legs. My legs were good enough to shut him up. Jack laughed. 'No one's talked to Robert like that before.'

I gave him a little piece of Kentish Town. The guy called Robert stayed quiet. Then he stood up ready to go. He turned around. 'I like Kentish Town. I like its brand of tough.'

I gave him another piece. 'And when you pride yourself on Where is she and Who is she, one up talk, perhaps you had better know it's AA talk. And if you already know it which I think you do give it another try.'

He walked out.

'No one ever talks to him like that.' Jack didn't hide his surprise.

'Who is he?'

'Only the head of the studio.'

As he walked with me to Ivan's gate he said, 'If you can speak to him like that, you can speak to Ivan. About my film. It's not about being turned down.'

It was.

'In a month I will have forgotten all about it. After a week they will say who's Ivan and after a month–' He paused. He was thoughtful. He said goodnight.

CHAPTER 12

TO SHOW I WAS A willing guest I swam in the pool every day and made a display of getting up Hollywood early – it seemed like my middle of the night – and I was approaching day 5 as a guest. I did not see the spider so far.

The day after my super dimensional eve at Jack's, or Johnny's as he was called by certain friends, his chef Tim waved to me from the hedge. He wanted to talk privately and waited while I climbed over the gate. I was no Jack Nicholson and he had to help.

'Don't let's set off any alarm systems,' he said. He was 28 and had worked for Jack since he left cookery college. His mother was a theatre actress. He was supportive in a non-obtrusive way and I couldn't say that about many people. 'Jack's depressed. He's in there with his shades on in front of the screen and never goes out. He wears shades everywhere.'

This was an arena of mixed problems in which I could make some lifelong regretted mistakes. I asked if there was an assistant who could help. Could the Ivan rejection be so important? In fact Ivan had forgotten the incident and was steeped in offers for scripts.

There were several assistants but Tim thought I could

straighten it out or else talk to the Italian girl Pia who was motherly. There was no point in talking to her as Jack was visible wearing his shades behind the shaded window. 'Just say you dropped by,' and Tim pushed me forward.

Jack led me straight into the TV room.

'Seen any spiders?' he asked.

'Have any in your pool?'

'I never look. The pool man deals with that.' He changed channels. He was subdued. I told him it's a beautiful day.

'Not in here it isn't.' I asked if he wanted to go out. 'Impossible. Going out, a thing of the past.' He said he was accosted wherever he went. He couldn't even go skating on the private ice rink without someone skating towards him carrying a script they wanted him to read. 'Then from the other side comes an agent with another goddamn script.'

'And in each one there's a goddamn 50,000 bucks as a reading fee.' I'd heard about this from my agent. To get the big stars to read you had to include a serious bribe called a reading fee, just inside the cover. For Jack it was probably double.

'Sorry. 100,000,' I said. Jack said this was wishful thinking from bitches. Then I realised what made him immediately noticeable. On all publicity these days, all covers and press items he wore 'the shades'. I told him to take them off.

'Impossible,' he said. 'They're the only protection I got.'

Tim waved urgently to me from the kitchen and I asked Jack if he needed anything. I think he said, the cemetery. 'Someone's just pulling up at the entrance. Someone you shouldn't see perhaps,' said Tim.

'His producer?'

'Yes, well no.' Tim hated to lie. 'The guy you insulted the other night.'

'Who is he?'

'Never mind him. The Italian assistant wants to see you.' He led me upstairs. I stopped. I had the answer. 'Tomorrow when you go to the market take him with you, without the shades. 50

bucks a bet either way he is hardly recognised.'

'What? Without his glasses?' Tim was uncertain.

'If they do we lose our 50. If they don't he loses his 50.'

'That won't happen.' The Italian woman had joined us. She said he would be mobbed.

'I'm prepared to lose the 50. At least it gets him out.'

Tim agreed to do it. He spent hours preparing divine food. Then Jack would come back from the studio too chemical, tired or depressed to eat. 'And I have to throw it away.' He admitted he was upset. 'Yet if I opened a tin of sardines Diana Ross would be there beside him.' He agreed it was worth trying and added a 50 note to mine and went downstairs.

The woman called Pia was at her End Game as she called it. 'It's since the day you arrived. He said Ivan wouldn't even think about his film offer. He Jack is directing it. It means a lot. To succeed with this. He's directed two films before. They were not appreciated. He acts in something and he's festooned with success. His own directing dives. It hurts. But it's more than that. But I can't get it. Not even the head of the studio and you know who I mean but keep quiet about that evening, can't change it.'

Why did Silvio come to mind? Didn't I have enough trouble? And lucky or otherwise he was not there. I asked if she'd heard of him.

'Heard? I love him,' she said warmly.

'He might know. He's wise sometimes. Let's call him.'

He wasn't difficult to find. He was moved in with the gang of boys upstairs in my house and slept in my bed. She told him the story. At least she got to half of it. He said to put me on.

'Ivan Moffat is respected. He is a real man. He's decorated from the war. He filmed the opening of the concentration camps with George Stevens. He's from the theatrical Sir Herbert Tree family. He has class. He fights for the freedom of speech.' Silvio couldn't say enough. 'Jack's the new brand. A lightweight fly by night. But one who's made it. He needs approval from this

73

giant of class, integrity and respect. And he can't get it. The rejection. God. Says it all.'

'So he has to change and be like Ivan? How can he?' said Pia.

'But he has to accept being Jack,' said Silvio.

The assistant took the phone. 'Mr Narizzano, can we get Ivan to make the 'no' sound like a 'maybe?'' she asked.

I heard Silvio laugh. 'Jack would see through that. It's another era, another way of thinking. Tell Jack I'll play the Ivan part.' More laughter. The Kentish Town boys were joining in.

'I bet you would,' I said. Silvio hung up.

The assistant was about to speak. There wasn't anything to say. Well we could make maybe one sentence. 'It can't be undone.' And another. 'Nothing to do.'

*

The next morning I looked out for Tim and expected he'd come to the gate. I saw the car and knew he was back from the market. I went to the furthest hedge and could see him moving in the kitchen. I called to him and he waved urgently, negatively, then ran down to meet me. Out of sight behind a tree he said one word, 'Disaster.'

'Oh shit. Droves of people?'

'You kidding?'

'The television? But did he have those glasses on?'

'Off.'

'So who recognised him?' He did pause. 'No one.'

'No one. We won the bet.'

'We haven't won anything. He doesn't want to see either of us. He gave me my 50 dollars back and also his for you to have as well.'

Mine had a spider drawn on the front.

'Maybe the timing,' I said. 'Too early.'

'There is no too anything in the farmers' market.' He ran back to the house.

CHAPTER 13

IT WAS A DULL DAY but bright enough to see the spiders. I could only point to them. Ivan was pleased as he watched this crowd crawl with speed, full of life, just above the water. 'They've made their nest right in the corner. Under that tree. Superb choice.' He was over enthusiastic. To goad me.

I went back inside but not for long. I heard the most unlikely sound. It was the munching of something bigger than a spider. This sound belonged in the forest. This was big. After munching came a cry of satisfaction. More munching, bigger this time. I crept to the corner of the room. This was escape from the zoo time. This was big. A giant bulldog? A buffalo? How big was a coyote? The fridge door was forced back. The animal had got its head inside and its sizeable rump was up in the air. 'What the fuck!' I ran out shouting for Ivan as a fridge rail emptied and crashed to the floor. 'It's got in. A wild animal.'

Ivan was calmly sitting by the pool writing. I said it was in the fridge.

'Honey, wild animals can't open a fridge door.'

'Why do you go for the niceties of life when we are in danger. It's huge. A buffalo.' I had never seen one but there was a first time for anything. I was ice cold with fear and reached for his hand. 'Is it a coyote?' All I knew about them was they could be aggressive. I had no idea what they looked like.

He asked what I was frightened of.

'It will eat me next.'

He got up from his work and walked steadily to the kitchen. I knew he had a shotgun meant for what he called squirrels in the bedroom. He stayed at the kitchen door. From where I stood I could see the rump and the creature had buttocks and was still munching. It didn't have a tail.

He turned and took my hand and we started towards the car. 'It's only Marlon,' he said.

Had a local wild animal been named after the superstar? No, this was the superstar who had unfortunately been mistaken for a wild animal. He told me to get in the car while he went to get his keys. The pool man was raking the side of the pool. I pointed with horror to the gang of spiders. The pool man didn't understand much English but he recognised fear. I hadn't got over the wild animal in the fridge and now there was speeding and scuttling of more than I thought.

'No worry lady. I take care of them.'

'You will not!' Ivan was back. 'Don't touch them. Understand.'

The pool man thought about it. 'You frightened. The lady frightened. I not frightened.'

Ivan pointed a finger at him. 'Leave them alone.'

'But they not frighten me. They not hurt me.'

'Do not touch those spiders.'

We got in the car. He started the engine and then leaned out. 'You leave them till I return.'

'Yes sir. I have no fear. You gentlemen. Fear.'

In the market Ivan bought a ton of irregular food. I asked who it was for but guessed it was for Marlon.

'He goes on a diet before filming. Then suddenly he gets that eating urge. It's just to fill him up. And then all bets are off. So lately he locks all the food cupboards and fridge. That's no good so he gives the keys to the staff. Then he asks for them back. The latest is he gives them the keys and warns them no matter what happens they must not give him the keys back. He even threatened to fire them if they gave into him and let him have the keys. He knew this was wrong. He's really a nice man.'

I knew that from seeing him in London during Chaplin's 'Countess from Hong Kong'. I thought of naming my first son Christian, after his son who I used to look after sometimes. I knew then the struggle with weight and diet.

'So in desperation he jumps over the hedge and breaks into my fridge. I pretend I don't know. So I buy extra food he seems to like.'

'Does it work?'

'Nothing works. Except the staff keep their jobs.'

When we got back there was a definite silence over the empty pool. It was very clean and still. Then the pool man proudly shouted, 'all done boss.'

Boss got out and with a heavy walk approached the edge. 'Where are they?'

'All gone boss. Not one left.'

Ivan's eyes closed with the horror of life.

'Don't be scared. They gone.'

Over the gate I saw a face. It was smiling hugely. Victory for Jack. All depression gone. He raised his thumb. Ivan quite stunned went back to the car.

'You not pay me extra for this boss. The other smiling man paid me. He said it was for the lady.'

The face over the gate disappeared. Time to retreat. Ivan went into the house. Spiders gone. I would be next.

Later Tim said Jack had done it for me. But I felt anger had been the real motive.

*

Too many calamities. Time for the fear laden guest to go to the

Sunset Marquis Hotel down the hill and start to work. We both needed the telephone and there was only one. So I said goodbye to Al Jolson's old guesthouse and went to write the outline for 'The Siesta' which became a movie in 1987.

Next time I saw Jack he wanted to talk about Ivan. We sat on the terrace of the Chateau Marmont Hotel. 'Henry Jaglom has the house next door. He funded and edited 'Easy Rider' which started me up. Look at that pool. But it's not Ivan's style. I know Ivan's old fashioned. That style he's proud to keep. When he goes it will go forever. No one has that way of doing things anymore. So I wanted to keep it on film as a record. That kind of loss. I hate it. And I blame him.'

Well I thought it better not to mention the drug side of things.

*

The Sunset Marquis Hotel in West Hollywood was popular with writers and performers but musicians in bands were largely not welcome after a couple of drug related incidents. The threat of their needing medical attention after making 'a night of it' discouraged the management and emergency staff now refused to attend 'willful destruction'. Silvio later told me about it. That would keep out a few of the people I was getting to know.

I wrote the revised movie outline of my book 'Siesta'. Up early the then producer who worked for Mick Jagger accompanied me on the wake up run which in my case was modified to fast walking. Yoga came next under a tree.

Then agent discussions, early meetings, breakfast, writing, more meetings, personal upkeep, Hollywood obligation – early to bed.

'I want you at your best. You're not in Kentish Town now.' Yes she knew of the zone. Jagger knew it. She said the movie deserved my best.

It was my third day and I flipped out to Hamburger Hamlet

with Ivan and games of backgammon and cards across Hollywood but the producer didn't miss the morning after appearance and she reminded me my expense account had only a few days left.

The meetings included Shelley Winters and Lauren Bacall, both interested in my novel 'Harriet Hunter' based on Ava Gardner and her disappearance with a bull fighter in Spain. It had to be a mysterious disappearance. When Ivan was in London I used to visit Ava Gardner with him for an evening of backgammon. I understood this was not her best time to play the lead in a movie.

Shelley directed a reading of my stage play at the Hollywood actor's studio near Schwab's Deli. This was a surprise and the best time. The stage play had been performed at the Cottesloe National Theatre. Shelley was a wonderful director and teacher and after a vegetarian lunch at 'The Source' West Hollywood where she was surrounded with friends and students, we went back to her place for backgammon. Ivan warned me it was better to let her win. No problem there. I could only lose.

'What's the matter with you?' he asked. 'No one can lose with Shelley.'

'She can't read the dice properly,' I said.

'If that's what you want to call it.'

But Shelley expected to win and thought I would be right to edit her biography. I promised her I would not be right for that but she brought out a substantial pile of papers and folders. It was terrifying. 'All that? It's a huge book,' I said.

'No this is not the book. This is chapter 1.'

Later I asked Ivan if he knew about this enterprise. He replied that she knew better than to show him.

The interviews for the tabloids came next. Dudley Moore, Roy Scheider and then I was offered a large sum by a women's mag if I could get an interview with Warren Beatty. It was unlikely as he was at the top of his career and rarely accepted interviews. But the star had known my former husband Michael

Chaplin who had appeared in one of his films and he agreed. I was invited to his house on the coast the following week. Also he was a friend of Jack Nicholson and knew the story of Ivan and 'The Two Jakes'. The fee for the interview would cover my life for a while.

The BBC documentaries about Hollywood followed. 'A Yes is only a Maybe', and 'The British in Hollywood' which included David Lean.

I would have loved to visit the legendary actor Joseph Cotton who lived just down the road from the hotel. He represented a Hollywood I loved especially 'The Third Man', and 'Citizen Kane'. I had been in the hotel nearly a week and getting ready to meet Ivan at Hamburger Hamlet. A tap on the door and for a moment I thought it was Jack. Just a moment that had escaped from the new rule, 'Take care of those feelings. They belong to the young'. I wore the new rules like a corset across my heart. In spite of the 99% chance of disappointment I opened the door.

Silvio propelled his way into the room. 'Get me a coffee.' He lay on my bed. 'You've been hard to find. Last time you stayed in Marina del Ray in the penthouse. What happened to you?'

He was referring to my invitation to write a woman's love story with pulse but no sex. The producer liked things clean. At least in the public eye. He was wealthy. Too much and vast to describe. He owned property, organisations and people. And he washed his hands a lot.

I got Silvio a snack and said I would have to go.

'Jack's back!' Silvio said suddenly. He sat up and peered out of window. 'He's out walking. I heard he was home hiding behind the dark glasses. He wants to get his mind on Faulkner and Scott Fitzgerald instead of the comic cuts those new boys think they are reading. They only look at the pictures.'

'Why do you put down those new actors? You said Jack Nicholson was a fly by night lightweight. Anything from 'Easy Rider' up is shit.'

'Read your film news. You'll see I'm using the star of 'Easy Rider' in my next film in Spain.'

'Dennis Hopper?'

'Don't be too quick on the draw. I've brought you a film. You write the Bud Cort part. And dialogue for the actress.'

'Here?'

'Here and in Canada.'

That film, 'Why Shoot the Teacher', got awards and acclaim but I did not end up writing it.

'You look good and light. As though you're in love. Who's the unlucky guy?'

Oh this was awful. I had learned how to change the subject. I said Joseph Cotton lived down the road and I would love to meet him. Silvio jumped up from the bed, finished the coffee and took my arm. 'Come on,' he said.

'You can't just walk in there.'

'Of course not.'

He took me straight to the right door and rang the system. They not only let him in, they were delighted to see him. And I to see Joseph.

Joseph Cotton talked of his true love, Ojai, a small settlement outside Hollywood where we could all be restored to who we really were. He had a house there and his dream was to start a centre. There were several spiritual groups in Ojai including my publisher the Theosophical Society. As he got older it sounded as though Ojai came to him in his dreams rather than he to it.

*

I met David Putnam on his way to the studio where Adrian Lyne the director he had discovered was standing in the doorway. He was auditioning 'Flashdance' and asked me to join them to watch Jennifer Beals, who later became the star.

Adrian used to live near me in London and knew Kentish Town well because he dropped his children off to play with mine. He was then in advertising and promotion. Then David discovered him. He said, 'I so miss Kentish Town. There is no culture here. No museums. Nothing happening. The sun comes down and they go to bed. The whole town empty. I can't stand it.' David calmed him. He said to just do 'Flashdance' and then they would reconsider. In fact he stayed for '9½ Weeks' and 'Fatal Attraction'. And then came the others.

*

The virus hit between one hour and the next. It was in the middle of the night. I was glad Silvio was there. He had made my sofa his bed and we lived on takeaways. Later in this day I would be going to the shore to interview Warren Beatty and my immediate financial security would be secured. I called for Silvio and he came in with a wet cold flannel and took my pulse. 'It's just a small bug.' He made cups of tea and crushed painkillers into the liquid. My throat was raw and swollen and I thought I was dying. I asked him to call a doctor.

'You must be joking. They won't come here. After all that's happened.' And he tried to divert me with lurid tales of OD'd musicians.

I told him he had better keep in the other room and not be vulnerable to this virus. It was no fun. He said simply that he wouldn't get it. Not a chance.

When it was daylight I called the producer and she was round within the hour. She asked for a doctor immediately. Not in this hotel. So Silvio got on the phone and the doctor showed up within minutes. Silvio was a kind nurse surprisingly. He was gentle with the situation. He said he'd had to look after several brothers and sisters.

Before the doctor could come into the room we had to prove this was not drug related. It seemed the virus overnight was spreading like a plague and two studios were shut down so Silvio said all this could not be drug related. Even in Hollywood.

The doctor gave a list of what he could do. It was a menu with prices marked clearly. I could be taken by ambulance into a care centre which would wipe out my LA earnings. Or I could go into the movie stars' private hospital where Bianca Jagger had gone and that would put me in debt for the rest of my immediate life. Otherwise he could do a round of blood tests and give me antibiotics to cut any possible infection. Silvio cut in. 'If everyone else in this town has it let her do what they do. They're not coming up with these prices.'

Then the producer said Bianca had gone into the hospital and Silvio asked if she was better.

'No.'

Before Silvio cut the doctor's visit short, he knew it was charged by the minute, I asked if there was a chance I could go down to see Warren Beatty at the shore.

'What are you going to do?' said the doctor. 'Kiss him?' I almost laughed.

'You can go. Get a limo. He might not let you in. But if you're giving him an interview he'll probably risk it.'

The producer said I would be better treated in London and she would fly me back the quick way, over the Pole. The doctor said it would keep his menu charges low. Silvio said it was better than lying at great expense in some elaborately decorated hospital. I spoke to Warren Beatty myself and he could hear my voice and said he was sorry and I could come if I wanted but there was smog today and probably wouldn't be good for me. I asked if I could see him the next day. Or after that?

'No. Tomorrow I leave for New York. I'm sorry. I look forward to seeing you. Say hello to Michael.'

On the third day Joseph Cotton phoned to see if I had escaped the virus.

'You will be alright when we get to Ojai. That is where we have to go.'

CHAPTER 14

'IF YOU WANT A FAVOUR from me regarding Jack Nicholson I'm the wrong director for that one.' Fred Zinneman laughed unexpectedly. I said it hadn't occurred to me. It hadn't.

'Because in my opinion he was not right for the lead in 'The Day of the Jackal' and Edward Fox was. Now Nicholson doesn't speak to me.'

We were sitting in Mount Street in smart London where he had his work flat. I was in there for two reasons. After all the work I had done with my lifetime lover Jose Tarres, a lot of it regarding the uncovering of the Kabbala Center in Girona, Spain, what had I found out? He had just read my books on that subject and finished with the aftermath of 'Julia', and now he wanted something different. Would I write the film outline of 'Portrait of a Marriage' about the love affair between Vita Sackville-West and Violet Kepple which had been published by Vita's son Nigel Nicolson. I had known Violet Kepple for years when I was a child and when I was growing up. Fred had heard from Ivan casually that I might be helpful. I was a new face in town with untouched information.

Fred said he was not sure he would get anywhere with those kinds of people. Anywhere? Nowhere is where I would get.

Surely the great Fred Zinneman would get into most places. Had Ivan told Fred about my small meeting with Jack Nicholson? I think Fred was looking for a little something more. He had a playful response to my confusion.

'You played your cards well with Jack but not your backgammon dice.'

'Meaning?'

'You kept yourself to yourself and interested him. You didn't say goodbye or say where you had moved to. He's not a mind-reader. Anyway he will come here for 'The Shining'. If I do something on the Catalan antifascist fight, he can't play the charismatic leader. Think about it. Remember your lover. Jack's too old.'

Here was one of the greats in cinema sitting opposite me, three Oscars, asking my advice. I said I would try with the Sackville-West family. I'll start with their son Ben.

'Tell them I will send a donation for their Sissinghurst Garden. The upkeep of those plants must be a strain on the pocket.'

'I don't think Nigel the brother will give the rights.'

Mr. Zinneman laughed. 'I think if we arrive in a Bentley with a cheque from 20th Century there won't be too much negotiation.'

I walked out feeling wonderful. It was a splendid day. Bacall was just up the street in the Connaught Hotel. I had good news for her too. 'Wonderful' didn't last.

Betty Bacall looked marvellous. She was the epitome of a star. She leaned over the stairs as I put one foot on the first step. How could I do what she could not. Get the money for her to play the lead in 'Harriet Hunter'. I told her I had the finance for the movie.

'He will put the money up today. He's in town.'

'No to Chaplin. This is not his style.'

Who else did I know?

'Elliott Kasner.'

She screamed and doors did open. 'That money! I would never touch it. Are you offering me their money! Don't you know who he is?'

I tried to say he came with very good credit. He'd backed Nicholson and Brando's film 'Missouri Breaks'. I never got up those stairs. She went back into her suite and slammed the door.

I asked the one I should have gone to in the first place. The agent Robbie Lanz said, 'Money is money. By the time it gets to you who knows where it comes from? I will handle the deal.' He paused. His accent was thick as bad makeup today. 'And we wash the banknotes together.'

Lauren Bacall was my favourite movie star always. She and Bogart, they were Hollywood. The dream place that had got me through a lonely childhood during the last World War. Except I did not feel alone. My father was away at war and my mother ill. The neighbourhood children were evacuated. There was only me and an older girl up the street. But I had the film star annuals and magazines.

*

Back in Kentish Town I got Nigel Nicolson's phone number from a mutual friend and I told him the wonderful news. The most heralded cinematic director wanted to film 'Portrait of a Marriage'. He didn't hesitate. No!

Did he know Zinneman? Was he familiar with the film 'Julia' and 'The Day of the Jackal'?

'No.'

'They will pay you–' I was in deep water here. How much would they pay?

'It's 20th Century Fox.'

'No.'

Round 2. 'But you wrote a book about it. Quite explicit.'

'That's different. I couldn't bear to see it on the screen.'

'It also has Violet Kepple who I knew in it–'

'Then you should have consulted a lawyer.'

'You will never get an offer like this. Do you want to think about it?'

'I will not entertain it.'

'Mr. Zinneman will come to see you.'

Before he hung up I told him one day it would be a film. But really bad. A recognisably bad series. I was right. A little more than a year later he needed money and the BBC took the rights and even asked me to collaborate on the story. My refusal was large but gave me no pleasure. I said they'd made Violet Kepple into a shop girl.

So off the phone with Nicolson and on a call to Fred. Two down. One to go.

'It's the rights,' I told him. 'And this family thing. Doesn't want it visual.'

'What about readers that have visual acumen?'

'I don't think the car and the cheque will do it.'

He did go to Girona. But he went via Madrid, a long way round. He didn't like aspects of the Jewish centre, coffee tables on the Star of David but he liked Jose.

CHAPTER 15

KENTISH TOWN AND I CAME into the house with my long-term forever friend Stu from Manchester who had had small roles in Silvio's productions. He had a face nobody forgot. They said he could have been a star but that didn't happen. He used dry wit instead of anger and needed it in his job as a Spanish travel rep. He was an excellent tap dancer. Also he was very funny. 'You get the joke right at the end,' was his today's prophecy. He told me to sit down. How I needed the calm of the house. We had just come back from the spiritual sanctuary where I had received hands on healing. Then I heard the voice of my son Tom, just out of sight in the kitchen. He was supposed to be at school. Stu got me a glass of water. 'He's got her with him,' he said softly. 'Be prepared for a surprise. That's one expensive healing wasted. And the fares each way.' He had a Northern prudence about life.

'He's supposed to be at school. In the science lab.'

'Exactly.'

All benefits of the healing evaporated and my heart was jumping. Stu said I would've been better off with a tranquilliser.

Tom was sitting with The Cat. I could see her in full daylight. She was holding a baby.

'I must have shit karma,' I said.

The Cat replied immediately. 'It's my sister's kid. Don't go stirring up things.'

I felt better standing up but didn't know what to do so I offered her a cup of tea. She didn't want milk. And did I have any biscuits. Tom didn't want anything. She said, 'Tom's good with babies.'

I put a tin of biscuits on the table. She said they were her favourite. 'So you get them from Harrods?'

I agreed I did.

'They are my favourite too. I always have a tin in for Tom.'

I didn't know what the hell to say. Did the baby look like my son?

'They're very expensive,' she said.

'I only get them if I have enough money,' I said not wanting her to think I had any.

'So you pay for them?' The Cat was shocked. Tom tried to signal. She quietened down.

'Do you pay for them then?' I asked.

'Of course not. I nick them. Three tins at a time.' She paused again. Was I really this much of a sucker?

'I'll get you a box or two. Next time I'm that way,' she said. She looked at Tom. 'Your mother pays money for them.'

Tom shrugged.

Silvio brought in the bags of shopping. 'Marks and Spencers are opening in the high street.'

I thought The Cat looked pleased about that. Then I really saw her, the face, the hair. She was absolutely beautiful. The way she moved as she gave the baby to Tom and looked through the food bags was compelling. 'You've been ripped off on this.' She took out the scones. And the tea.

'Harry Alan Towers wants you to play Eva Peron. So soon you'll be able to pay for your shopping. You start filming in the Summer. You've got an interview with 'Time Out',' Silvio told her.

'Never. To all of it.'

'You mean you don't want to be a movie star?' said Stu sarcastically. 'You'll be so lucky ducky.'

She didn't know how to take him but the Manchester accent was in his favour.

'I'll be Harry's emblem. That's what he said. I'll be photographed. But none of that talking stuff.'

'Are you sure you don't want to be a star?' said Stu. 'And go to Hollywood?'

'It's not my scene. I'm Kentish Town.'

*

Rami the boy without a family, took care of the house and he was a good kid. He said he wanted to do the best for the boys and the house because it was beautiful and Caldon helped him with the garden. He also said he felt a sense of gratitude that he had a home if only temporary. I felt moved by Rami and determined to keep the house as long as I could. I paid for him, as well as the others, to go to Ana Scher drama classes and Rami was doing well. Privately I asked him whose baby The Cat was carrying around. He laughed.

'It's not Tom's if that's what you think.' I did. 'She's too young to have a baby and also it would've shown in her stomach. She carries the baby around when she's begging. Gets more money.' He paused undecided. Then he said, you can't stop people taking gear. I knew he was thinking of Tom. 'Drugs are everywhere.'

'So how do people stop?' I knew the answer. When the pain gets too bad.

CHAPTER 16

I WENT TO PARIS TO do the research on Modigliani. I had first heard his story from a nurse in a medical department when I was waiting for one of the Kentish Town boys. 'You should read this,' she said.

It was a small piece in a newspaper, maybe two paras. A Modigliani painting had sold for a record price in the US. The article described his life and death. He was destitute, failed and never sold one painting except to a friend, Carco. He was an alcoholic, talented beyond measure, unrecognised. The last week of his life he lay abandoned in the studio in Montparnasse, looked after by his companion and love Jeanne Hebuterne. It was an icy cold winter and they had only sardines to eat. She was about to give birth to their second child. The first was in care. Modigliani's prediction during that last week, 'death makes the market' was to come true. He died of tuberculosis and meningitis in the charity hospital on January 24th 1920. Jeanne unable to live without him fell to her death from the window, the baby unborn inside her. Within a year his pictures started selling. And now in the 1980s his work reached the highest price ever.

I felt icy cold after I read it. Was it that the story was not unknown to me? I phoned my publisher and got a deal before I even stopped speaking. I went to Paris for the research and it was as though I opened my hands and the information and other material was placed with grace upon them. I met people from that time that were supposed dead. I wrote the story first as a novel, 'Forget Me Not'. It got some special reviews. I got a call from the Lanz office. 'Alan Ladd Jr wants to buy the rights. You get to write the first draft of the screenplay. You take the next plane. Your ticket is already bought, first class.'

It was red carpet all the way and I went to the Hollywood meeting within hours of arrival. They were that keen.

Three men sat in a row behind a long desk. Alan Ladd Jr was in the middle and on his left an Italian who did most of the talking. The third, still practising how and when to smile, ran the studio. There were several copies of the book laid out in front of them.

'You had some great reviews. You write like Daphne du Maurier some say.' The Italian jumped up excited. 'You've dug out the truth of that last terrible week that no one wanted to talk about ever. I am Italian too you understand. When I finished this book I cried. Robby Lanz' office knew what to do. They gave the deal to us.'

We were given the usual coffee and an assortment of easy to eat delicacies. 'How many screenplays have you written Mrs. Chaplin?' asked the studio head. He started making notes. Only the 'Eva Peron' was supposed to go onscreen.

'Do you think so?' said the Italian. 'Silvio sold it and the deal onto a US based company some time ago. I expect you got your share.'

I didn't.

I tried not to look anything other than glad.

'There's a thing called Karma,' said the Italian. 'But it's still your work. You wrote it.'

Why hadn't that bastard told me but I couldn't let this deceptive bastard ruin my success.

'The Siesta' was written by the producer's wife Patricia Louisiana Knopf, writer of 'Nine and a Half Weeks'. I started to mention my books and TV film but they moved onto 'The Deal'.

Alan Ladd Jr introduced it with a studied calm. He told me they would buy the rights of the book outright and I would be paid for the first draft. 'You don't get option payments with us. We don't deal with low figures. This is what we propose.' And Alan Ladd Jr came up with a figure I had not so far in my life got near. 'That's for the book. Now here's your commission for the first draft.' Another figure that would change my life.

The Italian asked who I thought should play Modigliani. They went through actors, then actresses, then directors. They were keen on a new Mexican director.

More coffee, more compliments. When did I want to write the screenplay and where? Hollywood? Kentish Town? It was all becoming unreal.

Another round of juice and some mineral water. I would be put up at the Beverly Hills Hotel while they did the deal with Lanz. Then they stood up. 'Oh there is just one thing.' Alan Ladd Jr turned the pages of one of the books. He was obviously going to get me to sign it. He got to the last page. 'The artist dies wonderfully written.' The others agreed. 'But you have her Jane, the mistress—'

I immediately corrected his pronunciation.

'Jumping out of a window with the baby still in her.'

I agreed that was right.

'It won't go down in Texas.'

I'd heard this before. Did Jack's producer say that? Why did Texas dominate US thinking. So I asked why Texas was so important.

'It has to work in Texas. It's got to be something they understand morally. It's the money you see.' Alan Ladd Jr closed the book. 'So can you give us another ending.'

'We're wide open for whatever you give.' The Italian opened his arms wide.

'As long as it's a happy ending.'

We were all still standing.

'But Jeanne is unable to bear his dying and couldn't go on,' I told them.

'It won't work in Texas. They have strong conservative values.'

I named a handful of shocking films. Then I added 'The Exorcist'. I was sure that had been shown in Texas.

'A woman jumping out of the window with the baby inside her.' The Italian put his hands over his ears. 'Impossible.'

'Impossible!' the head of the studio agreed.

'So what about 'Rosemary's Baby'?'

'It's not Texas,' said Alan Ladd Jr.

We stayed for a moment in silence. Then I said you want me to write an ending. 'What about she jumps out of the window then lands on a rebounder unexpectedly under the window and is transported back into the room again.'

Was I taking the mick? They all looked at me not sure.

'Can she wait to have the baby first?' said Alan Ladd Jr. 'There's a lot of Catholics in the US.'

'And they buy cinema tickets,' said the Italian. 'Let's not have them die at all?'

'But this tragedy of Jeanne and her baby dying there in the street is the grand sacrifice. It was the drama that stayed with everyone in that world. It attaches to each one of Modigliani's works. It's the story buyers buy with the picture. It's the gold wrappers from Harrods. It's the joining of the ultimate story, the sacrifice, that makes his work continue to grow phenomenally. Without that he is just another painter.'

'I like it,' said Alan Ladd Jr. 'I wish I could do it. Why didn't she just give birth before she jumped?'

Didn't I ask the question of Modigliani's family who'd come up from Italy to meet me in Paris. They were realistic and joyous. Madame Shalitte, witty and right to the point, in fact she had some of her uncle's charisma, said, 'Why would the French Catholic girl stay and bring another baby into the world. She's already got one she can't manage. She's unwanted by her family. What's the point of waiting and going through all that pain of birth and loss of him. For what?'

The studio head started moving pages on the table. I had one last offering.

'Ok. She's in the room pregnant and then she isn't. An uproar in the street. She's fallen pregnant but we don't see that. She's dead but she's reached up to a beautiful light. We're in a spiritual place now, where we go after death. And she is suddenly there carrying her child and there's a sound of bells and a man walks towards her. Modigliani as he was young and good looking and he holds out his hands to her.'

Pause.

'So they reconnect on the other side of life.'

'Not in Texas they don't,' said the studio head.

*

I stayed one night in a hotel but not the Beverly Hills. I was now downgraded and Texas had got the better of me. The assistant at the Lanz office came along with a book. They say you can do this story as a first draft screenplay. A girl on an Eastern Island which is at war jumps into the sea and swims to safety. She finds a boat and sails across many oceans arriving in the US.'

'Is that it?'

She said I could write it in that hotel, all expenses paid. I replied, 'Texas won't like it.'

CHAPTER 17

IVAN, IMPRESSED THAT I HAD held my integrity and turned down fantastical sums invited me to the Beverly Hills for dinner to celebrate what in his view was my success. When I'd had some sleep we would sit at the centre table with every eye in the room upon us. He had known Alan Ladd Jr's father the actor who had starred in 'Shane', a movie Ivan made with George Stevens in the early 50's. He didn't like Alan Ladd Jr's company and the very day of the meeting the Italian was arrested.

Instead of going back to the hotel I went to Barney's Beanery with Orson Welles and he said we would never forget each other. How could we after meeting in Silvio's disaster film a couple of years before. He remembered how we were both guests in Silvio's castle and somehow Silvio managed to get all his guests into a movie, 'The Sky is Falling'.' Silvio said it would be shot economically but just how economically he did not say except it would be made and completed in his home in the south of Spain.

After three days of shooting in the local area we and the other performers realised we were being housed and fed not by Silvio but the local tradesmen and the castle supposedly Silvio's was rented. On the fourth day before dawn we were told to creep and then run to the local airstrip where a plane was ready to leave, engines running.

'What the hell!' said Orson remembering it with mixed feelings. 'I can creep but I can't run. I thought it was part of the film.'

'So did I,' I realised suddenly.

'All the drinking and meals and nights out and transport came out of the tradesmen's pocket and these were real Spanish from Andalusia and by day four when the money had not been flown in as promised they were prepared for trouble.

I wondered if there ever had been any money. Orson said the money had been in place but late and there was no insurance. And he thought he was there on holiday. We both remembered the morning wakeup call. 'Move fast. Take passports.' Creeping, then running the crew made it deftly to the airstrip but the locals were up to that and there was the sound of gunfire. Most of us got onto the rented plane but then realised Orson was not there. We waited and he came flat out just reaching the runway. The police reached it too. The plane started moving and I remembered Orson trying to catch onto one wing and we hanging out trying to grab him.

'You got so near,' I said. I could even hear the gasping breath as he ran arms outstretched. The plane took off and the last sight I had was Orson being stopped by the police.

'They put me in a cell. Silvio owed quite a few pesetas as it was known in those days. Harry Alan Towers bailed me out. I think I lost a few kilos that day. That's what Silvio said. He said I saved your living from being taken from you. You were putting on fat and your TV ad for sherry was gonna be dropped. I saved your life.'

I asked if he still spoke to him.

'Of course. It was a life stunt. It could've been a good film. Of course he made it later with Dennis Hopper. Silvio's a charlatan but then so am I.'

We agreed we dressed artistically and not for Hollywood.

People came up to him asking for his autograph or just to stare. He said we should go down to the coast and have a proper meal. I asked him if he played backgammon. He said no. I said thank god.

*

Talking to Orson Welles I realised I was powerless over my Modigliani book sale and as Robert Evans, he now had a name, predicted, I would not get it past the 'M' in Modigliani. Not into the studios with that ending, Orson told me. 'It's really about her, Jeanne Hebuterne,' he continued. 'So why don't you write it as biography.'

And that's what I did when I got back to the UK. Virago published it in 1990 as 'Into the Darkness Laughing'. I also wrote it as a play for Sunday night radio and as a stage play in Paris, Spain, Norway and festivals in Europe and the UK.

But that night eating at the beach the subject turned again to Silvio and how he got away with so much. 'It's not that people forgive him,' said Orson. 'He doesn't know he's done anything wrong.' He asked if I still saw him.

I didn't know how to answer. I would be suing him after the deceit he pulled on me with 'Eva Peron'. 'It was my script. I had written it. How could he sell it on to a company who then won a prize and not tell me.' I had tried to ring Silvio but his phone was on message and so was mine in Kentish Town. I left a message promising him legal action. I found myself telling Orson the whole story. He asked what kind of contract I had. I said Harry Alan Towers dealt with it. He laughed and said to forget any lawyers. He asked how much I got paid. I remembered the 200 and some more when Silvio collected the final draft.

'Don't think of suing Silvio. He has good lawyers. He needs them.'

I said again it was my writing.

'Not any more. I looked it up. It's got a man's name and Silvio is the co-writer. I looked at the original writing. Yours. And it's good. But now we have second draft writers. Yours is better but another producer is on it so it's been sold and better forget it. It will be one of Harry's boys. It got a prize in a festival and there is now, pasted over, shots of a new star. A girl from Kentish Town.'

So The Cat had seen the light.

I said to Orson that he'd been left high and dry in Spain and how did he feel about it. He said again that Silvio was a real talent but who knows where that led him.

So what paper or contract did you actually sign?' he insisted. I couldn't remember one. 'I think I trusted him.'

His laughter was long, loud and marvellous.

He sat thinking about his own problem, his reels of film being taken by the deceptive government that pretended to lose them on a secured boat to another shore. He said it was his best film so I assumed it was 'Citizen Kane'.

'No, no. 'The Magnificent Ambersons'. The government had to steal that film because of the coded secrets it carried. They had admitted as they called it 'shipping it to safety' somewhere offshore but it had sunk without trace. Warren Beatty is giving good help.' And he mentioned Henry Jaglom the cousin of my Kentish Town friend Caldon.

'They have set up a way to lift it from where it is buried.'

I said the water might affect the condition of the content of the barrels. What I really meant to say was 'will it go down in Texas?' My head was full of that phrase and I was not in a good mood. He said, 'Of course they would not put those barrels in water. They're buried onshore.'

When Warren Beatty did retrieve the barrels they were empty.

CHAPTER 18

I KNEW IVAN HAD GOT the best table and every eye would be upon us. I was wearing Roman rope sandals and a yellow cotton dress. I noticed Ivan's eyes resting on its lack of adornments. It was simple and beautiful. Ms Selfridge, 12 pounds. He poured a couple of drinks and I could hear Jack's laughter. He was calling me. He was leaning over the fence. 'How do you feel about frogs?' he laughed. 'We're out of spiders today.'

Ivan sighed. 'I'll go and get ready. You do the same.'

I told him I was ready.

'Not for the Beverly Hills. Not in that dress. You surely have another one with you.'

'It's pure cotton.'

'And creases like hell. Go and look in the mirror,' he said.

There were a few creases in one small area. He told me I hadn't had it ironed properly or any cleaning treatment for the fabric. He went to the phone and I could hear him cancel the reservation. One of the ropes broke and the Roman sandal became loose. Ivan came out more casually dressed carrying his car keys. I asked where we were going.

'Hamburger Hamlet.'

He opened the car door for me. 'But I thought we were

going to the Beverly Hills.'

'Not in that dress you're not.'

I thought I heard Jack laughing over the fence. It was only a low flying bird. I was tired and I was perhaps feeling sorry for myself. I was definitely angry. I ran into the living room and phoned Orson Welles. I told him the situation. I hadn't even finished the story when he said, 'I'll take you. I'll come and get you.' I started to tell him Ivan's address.

'I know it. 10 minutes.'

I told Ivan Orson was coming to get me and take me to the Beverly Hills.

'Don't be ridiculous. Don't add craziness on top of all this.'

By now the sandal was off my foot altogether.

Ivan got out of the car. 'You might as well take the other sandal off as well. We will get some food sent in. Orson Welles won't come and get you. He's got other things to do.'

The electric system at the gate sounded and Ivan pressed the button to open.

Orson's car was a wagon filled with equipment. Orson wasn't looking much better than me. He wore a creased shirt over his trousers. But he had an elegance of spirit that dismissed all the creases and broken sandals.

They shook hands and Ivan offered him a drink which he sipped. 'Have to get the English girl some food. Great to see you.'

I thought Ivan had a look of pity as he saw the tough wagon lumber its way to the gate. What restaurant could let us in? Not even the Hamburger Hamlet. 'Where are you going?' I asked as he went down the hill towards Hamburger Hamlet.

'The Beverly Hills. Isn't that where you want to go?'

'He's cancelled the table.'

'I think we don't need to use his credentials to survive.'

Arriving at the Beverly Hills he jumped out and threw the keys to the valet to park. He let me out and didn't seem to care that I was barefoot. I was nervous. He took my hand. 'After all you've been through at the edge and managed to survive,

I wouldn't have thought that this was such a deal.' He put his arm around me. They greeted him like the king. Central table? Absolutely. No mention of Ivan. No fifty dollars expected by the head waiter. Everyone stared. They loved him.

The meal was interrupted by his admirers. Even Robert Evans came to say hello. Others wanted to talk to him. There was no bill. He was invited right and left to come for drinks, an opening, even a weekend, as we left the centre for the circumference.

Ivan told me later that Orson normally ate at the exclusive Ma Maison. And Liz Taylor and Richard Burton had to wait outside and ask the owner if they could come in and say hello to Orson Welles. Did he even notice? He noticed me. For a while.

CHAPTER 19

SILVIO SQUEEZED IN THE LIFT with Quentin Crisp still carrying the scrabble board. We had just left our host, screenwriter Win Wells on the 39th floor and I sincerely hoped we would descend without interruption to the ground. I kept my concerns to myself. The lift was crowded, hot, but Silvio did not want to wait for it to go down and come up again 39 floors. He didn't like the idea of waiting. It was as simple as that. We were mid NY on Madison and I supposed this lift was a child's climbing frame compared with the real elevators uptown. Quentin insisted his manager – real job description, bodyguard – came too. 'I can't go anywhere in New York without him. Everyone recognises me.'

'So why don't you wear dark glasses?' I suggested. Silvio, remembering the Jack story, laughed. Quentin after a skirmish at the scrabble board was not speaking to me. He had said after that game that he despised me. Quentin's manager was Romanian, a gambler, with a penchant for poker which took away most of his nights. He knew little about the world of writing and less about the gay existence of his employer. Silvio pushed the manager into the crowded lift and kept his finger on the pause button. The manager apologised as his natural weight size reduced everyone's space. Silvio danced in and out of the lift effortlessly to gather the last of his group. 'Ready to go,' and he took his finger off and as the doors started to close Charlotte from Kentish Town rushed between them, not wanting to be left out and crammed herself in by holding onto my hips. She was thin enough just to get away with it.

One of the occupants complained. 'We're well over the limit.' Another said fourteen people was the max. Another said it was these last thoughtless stragglers getting in that put everyone at danger. There were other bigger lifts around the side of the building so why didn't these stragglers go round there. Silvio told him to go there himself and take one of them if he was so keen on it. The atmosphere was heading for trouble.

'It's only 39 floors,' said Charlotte, her voice very English and brisk. 'And we've done 10 of them surely.'

Silvio laughed. 'You're only trying to appease this lot. They are frightened rabbits.'

She said she would get out at the next stop. 'It's my fault.' She was shaking.

'Nothing like a lift to dig out all your character faults. Why take all their fear and blame yourself,' said Silvio.

Her eyes closed. Her hands clasped together, lips moving, and I assumed she was praying.

Quentin was in the mood to perform and his manager kept saying, 'Quieten it Quentin. You're not on.'

'He's always on,' said Silvio. Then came a sudden silence that Silvio found boring. 'Furs are out,' he said decisively.

I couldn't see the connection with Quentin. Then I realised the blonde behind me was wearing a sizeable fur. She was highly perfumed which in that lift was a big statement. Silvio looked at the coat. 'It's last owner died in it.'

'Says who?' The man had a rough voice. He was squeezed behind the woman out of sight.

'This lift doesn't seem to be moving,' said the first complainant.

'You're right,' said Charlotte. They all agreed. Quentin's manager tried for calm.

'It's just a smooth up to date lift. Not many in this area.'

'So is my finger,' said Silvio. 'Smooth and up to date. I forgot I had it on the stop button.' He took it off and the lift lurched and started a not altogether smooth descent. No one was sure. Was it going up?

'When we get out I'm going to sort you out,' said the first complainant.

'He's mine,' said the one with the rough voice.

'If we get out,' Silvio laughed. 'It's stopped.'

It had stopped because a passenger on floor 28 was waiting to get on. The doors partly opened and a woman waited with heavy shopping. 'Not this time lady,' said Silvio. But two people in our cluster desperately wanted to get out and tried to push the fur wearer out of the way. Too late. Doors shutting. The lift was full of apologies and aggression.

'I'd walk to hell to get off this thing,' said Quentin.

Silence so Silvio had to say, 'I don't like standing next to a murdered animal.'

A mistake. The man pressed himself in front of the girl. He was big and he worked out and he was no stranger to a fight. I dug Silvio on his side in warning.

'When the lift stops I'll sort you,' the man told Silvio. 'You're gonna wish you were covered in fur to soften the damage I'm going to do.'

'Go tell it to your psychiatrist,' Silvio replied. He chose to add, 'The smaller the dick the bigger the talk.' He decided to look at me and give a friendly smile.

'We are not together,' I said to the lift occupants. And to God. Charlotte nudged me. 'Let's get off.'

'Off where?'

'The next stop. Now. Press the button.'

'But we have to get down 20 flights. We've only just passed 26.'

Silvio seemed to get his first good idea. 'But what if the animal she's wearing died a natural death? That makes it all different.'

Floor 23. Doors open. Doors shut. The rough man was short on words but clear on intention. Silvio was going to wish he could have an animal's death. I believed Silvio could always get himself out of it in the end. I remembered lifts brought out the worst in him. How could have I forgotten Pier Paolo Pasolini recounting his lift story with Silvio. And laughing.

Floor 24. Doors open. Doors shut.

'We're going up,' said a middle aged woman. 'Let me take over pushing those buttons. That guy isn't right. He's pressed up.'

Lift stop. Floor 22. Doors shut.

'It's only the lift's mistake.' The group were relieved. Everything back on track.

'A lift that goes down and then up and everyone's pleased. I'm with a lot of losers,' said Silvio.

A silent space between floors. Charlotte nervous. Quentin wrapped in his own thoughts. I was anxious as hell. Silvio was Silvio. Quentin suddenly spoke. 'This must be how they felt as the Titanic went down.'

The lift stopped at 21. The doors did not open.

'I could never be in a building like this,' Quentin confessed. 'I've got a thing about heights. And now it's about crowds.'

'Unless they're audience,' said the manager.

'That's why you live in the Chelsea,' said Silvio. 'No crowds there. Out of date. It's a has-been.'

The blonde spoke. 'Oh are you famous! I think I've seen you.'

'I don't like a bottle blonde coming on to me,' said Quentin pretending to be offended.

'Remember the boyfriend,' said Charlotte. 'We're not out of here yet.'

Silvio turned to the girl. 'You look like Sharon Stone.' He

gave her a Silvio special, the smile that showed his teeth.

'I'm thrilled!' She was happy. Her voice rose, the happier she got. 'D'you hear that Morty? He says I'm a movie star.'

'Says who?' said Morty.

'I'm thrilled.' Her voice was high.

'I've never heard a woman coo before,' said Silvio.

What was it about lifts in New York that brought out the dangerous worst in him.

Luckily she didn't know the word 'coo' and thought it was another compliment.

'Who does he think he is? A movie director?' said Morty.

'You must be a psychic,' said Silvio. The lift stopped. Floor 17.

Silvio didn't have much time.

She was too thrilled for Morty to interfere. Maybe. By the time the lift touched ground Silvio and she had to be closing a deal. Eager to live Silvio was all charm. 'I want to audition you for my new film, 'Why Shoot the Teacher?' You'd be wonderful for the schoolteacher.'

'Oh my. Do I get shot?'

'Maybe. But you sure thrill them before that.'

Murmuring in the lift. People had seen him in magazines, knew about the film and Bud Cort the actor.

'There's one problem,' said Silvio, at his most pleasant. 'What about Morty? Will I be alive when I get out of this lift? Will I stay alive long enough to put you in the film? Will 'Loot' be the last one I make?'

She hung onto his hands. 'Yes, yes. I'll even take my coat off.'

We fell out of the lift one way or another.

They stood in the passage close to making some kind of a deal. I could see he really liked something about her. She was a natural, apart from the hair. He gave Morty a slap on the back. 'We're cool aren't we? It's just the stress of the lift.' Morty did the easy thing and agreed it was.

Quentin hugged me. 'I'm sorry I insulted you during our game.' He felt more eager about scrabble than I did. He was the Ivan of scrabble. He only made worthwhile words. He would rather pass than make a word like I had. 'Mat? What is 'mat?' I can't play with someone that lays 'mat'.' He put all his tiles on the board as he went out and won on 'MARZIPAN'. He said I was a scrabble suicide.

I think I got offended but the journey by lift had come afterwards and all words – mat, cat, marzipan, were forgotten.

*

New York. I was going to a meeting with a top producer who had asked to see me. My new agent at Lanz had just sold my autobiography 'Albany Park' and the following one, 'Another City' to Saint Martin's Press, a classy US publisher. The idea was I combine the two books into a first draft screenplay where I the protagonist could be in the movie as storyteller. My time at RADA would come in useful.

All I remember about walking towards 92nd Street was I wore yellow and the car which stopped at the door I was approaching was purple with a touch of pink and the guy was in a huge hurry and he jumped from the car and left it, doors swinging open, maybe engine still running, as he ran into the building and sped into the lift. I followed him in and the doors gripped shut. I looked at the car still visible abandoned like a colourful metal insect strangely alive with waving wings outspread. He crouched in the corner of the lift and I assumed he was on the run and not dangerous. He looked familiar. He spoke. 'Is that vehicle flash, abandoned, the real me? Or is this, huddled over one, in the dark of the lift?'

I didn't answer so he decided I couldn't answer.

'Are you going to be long in there?'

I didn't know.

'Because I desperately need to see him. So I hope you're not

112

going to spend a whole session on your childhood.'

Confused I asked who he was seeing.

'My psychiatrist of course. What time did he say he would see you?' He sounded so worried I would've given him my place willingly if I was seeing him.

'He's a shrink?'

'Well of course. Isn't that where you're going?'

I felt proud to say no. I was also proud to say I was going further up to the producer everyone wanted to see.

'Oh yes.' He straightened up as though this information belonged with the colourful car. The lift had stopped and he held the door open.

'I hope I haven't alarmed you. Mister Maybe upstairs will alarm you more.'

And he was gone.

I almost knew who he was. Then I thought maybe, after all the trouble I was having with Silvio and lifts, I should see a shrink. Forget the 'Mister Maybe' career and get some help.

The producer was positive but cautious. At one point he looked out of the window. 'They're late taking his car and parking it in the garage.'

I asked if this had happened more than once.

'Of course. Sometimes every day. He has that exuberant car which is the real him. Maybe. And the other covered up in a dark corner of the lift.'

'What's his name?'

'Woody Allen.'

Of course.

CHAPTER 20

AS 'THE TOMBSTONE' HAD PREDICTED when Jack was disappointed about his film, Ivan's 'The Thorn Birds' director would walk off and it would become a TV series. Ivan he predicted would also not be working. I did wonder what he'd seen for me. Ivan did need support because he suggested I get in touch with Jack Irish, the man with the towers in Marina del Rey.

I expected Ivan's new project could interest him as Jack Irish did fund projects.

I remembered only too well when I stayed with him and survived those scorchingly early farmhouse breakfasts he so enjoyed sizzling up before 6 am. 'I never trust a man who doesn't come to my table for his breakfast before 6.15 am.' I remembered, I couldn't forget one humid morning throwing open the back door and there on the dustbin lid sat a man. He was perched ready to be up for the right moment. I asked if he wanted to see anyone. He nodded. He was good looking and familiar. I went back to the kitchen and told Jack Irish that a man was sitting on the dustbin. He replied that he wanted me to pass the olive oil. I sat on a chair overcome by the steam from the cooking in the early hour. But there were worse off than me and one of them was sitting on the dustbin. I asked if I could give the man some money.

'How much you got?' And Jack Irish got a good laugh out of that. 'He's only an actor.'

He was an actor called Clint Eastwood. He wanted money to make a movie. Jack Irish had been involved with 'Play Misty for Me'. Jack Irish gave him some funding and the film was unforgettable.

There were two other difficulties, apart from the obligatory early breakfast, that needed careful handling. One, his girlfriend. She was straight, good, a schoolteacher, pure apparently, devoted to him. The other, the girls that arrived in the penthouse between 5 and 6 some evenings. These were ex-beauty queens. Miss US. Miss World occasionally. It was apparently hard getting work after their well noted acclaim. I supposed that explained their current job.

They were entertained in the central lounge downstairs and all the upper rooms circled above this space. My bedroom was one of them. There was only one way out. A short flight of noisy wooden stairs that led to the side of this lounge and the exit. If I was upstairs and playtime was on I had to wait sometimes an hour until the fun was over and I could creep out through the overly used lounge. I missed several meetings and meals being stuck in my room. I did consider just walking down the stairs and to the exit. An 'excuse me' might cover it. Did the girlfriend know of the other side of Jack, he never mentioned his 6 pm entertainments.

I had to get out.

The girlfriend got me out. She was possibly jealous of me to begin with. Then she thought I was after his money. No chance there. A Fort Knox job all round Jack Irish and women. But she wanted money. Not for herself but to build a nursery school for children with some difficulties that would be inaugurated in Jack's name. I could never remember which difficulty and didn't believe it anyway. He thought she was a beautiful person for struggling with this so needed operation.

'She needs money more,' I said. My number was up. But I was suddenly sick of it all, the fulsome false patter she gave him.

She said, 'I would never ask my soulmate for one buck to help me, so help me God.' He nodded in sweet agreement. He'd gone for it.

'Just knowing him is enough.'

Then she turned and stroked his face and head. 'I wish you were my little mouse and I could cuddle and stroke you in my pocket all day.' He loved it.

I cracked up laughing. I just didn't say hookers in London said better shit than she did.

She left for work and I said I'd leave. I went to my new producer Alain Chammas who was taking care of my book 'Harriet Hunter' which was still doing the rounds. Alain from the Middle East came from a family of carpet sellers. They knew their business and he spent the money. Everyone in Hollywood knew of him at that time. He would bake some effective doped cakes loved by Bertolucci. I would see him there with his wife Clair Peploe who I knew from London and Bertolucci laughed so much at the stories of Jack Irish and the women that he fell off the side of a sofa and strained two ribs. Alain liked spur of the moment entertainment. A 'copter journey to Vegas to gamble. A visit to a fat farm to see an overeating star. Getting a wild actor, also drunk, onto a straight TV show which became the talk of Hollywood, at least for 24 hours, was his best thrill. Alain had given my book to two actresses, Lee Remick and Romi Schneider and they had both been keen and then passed away.

He had phoned me with the news. 'Lee died on it.' I thought he was using the parlance in Hollywood for someone who was no longer interested and had died on the project. I said it was only an actress saying no so get another. There's loads of actresses out there.

He breathed sharply. 'You London girls are tough.' I asked what he meant.

'Lee is dead.'

Oh god.

He told me to be careful of Jack Irish and he would be the one in a position to know. He suspected anyone close to the billionaire would be tracked and bugged. 'Maybe I'm just psychic.'

He was psychic.

Maybe the girlfriend schoolteacher was partly good or just putting things in more trouble with 'the mouse' as he was now known by the Bertoluccis.

'Such a shame you're leaving.' The schoolteacher even sounded false. 'He wanted to do so much for you. But I advise you to do one thing. Get him a present. He will expect that.'

My career wasn't going any better than my other friends in Hollywood. It was all delay and the clock hands went backwards like an old style Jewish clock. So I had a half day between meetings. I went quickly to the best store to buy a present but what did I give the man who could buy himself anything. I would have found it easier in New York as I didn't know 'those' shops in LA. I phoned Alain Chammas and he said seriously, 'A book of expensive porn and another of all the sexual positions and how to get them without dying.'

I could ask Ivan but I realised I never gave him a present. Then my intuition came full on. 'An Irish linen tablecloth.' After all he said he was Irish and it might remind him of his childhood.

I got a cab that took me to a shop and I asked the driver to wait. He admitted afterwards he didn't know what an Irish tablecloth was. We went to another store. I kept saying I need a top expensive boutique. 'You know where the rich people go.' He didn't. He was from across the border and just about spoke the language. 'Where would you go for a good present?' I asked him and then I realised of course he would not know where to go. He did take me to where he went for his family birthdays. An hour wasted in there. Then I got it. 'A backgammon set.' Back into Beverly Hills for that. I also bought two expensive glasses.

The long shopping exercise took the whole day and I missed the second meeting. The girlfriend was waiting in the kitchen. Jack Irish was in his office. She helped me in with all the bags. 'My, my, you're a shop-a-holic as well.' Curtly I asked what that meant. 'As well as a good writer of course.'

Never!

But suddenly looking in those bags she took a kind of pity on me. All this cheap shit that he couldn't even see without being offended. She had known the result before I had even started out. How would I know the present she had suggested. 'One with your heart in it.' She picked up the backgammon set and threw that to one side. The two glasses. Even I could see they were wrong. The present setting brought out their cheapness. She picked on the Irish linen tablecloth and fingered the fabric. She went swiftly to the label. 'Made in Ireland. Nothing about linen here.' She swept the lot into a rubbish bag. 'I'll take it to the charity dump.' Then she saw the big-faced Jewish clock with its hands going back hiding under the table like a shy pet. She shivered. 'For Jack Irish? Never!' She heard him approaching and bundled the rubbish bag under her things and I was grateful. She quickly murmured, 'Give him one of your books, signed.' That took one minute.

The shopping trip one day.

*

Months had passed when I phoned Jack Irish and he agreed to see Ivan. We spoke together for some time and he was soft voiced and pleased to hear from me. Ivan chose our meeting venue, 'The Polo Lounge'. 'All those who are trying to get into the movie business think it's the place to go.'

'He's not trying to get in. He is in. He buys the 'in'.' Ivan had no respect whatsoever for an untalented wannabe. No matter what the bank account. I told him to wait until he saw Jack Irish. I reminded him he needed to see him. 'Not the other way round.'

'There's nothing like an ardent amateur.'

We approached the entrance to The Polo Lounge and I think it was then I remembered Alain Chammas's warning. 'He'll know what you're doing. He will bug it if he doesn't. Be careful.'

A large car sped past to the front of the queue. The number plates appalled Ivan. JACK IRISH.

Ivan couldn't sneer enough. 'Of course it has to be a ridiculous spectacle.'

I didn't know what to answer.

'He will ask for the Eggs Benedict. They always do when they go to the Polo Lounge. He won't know what to ask for so that will be it. I bet you money on that.'

In the entrance two well-dressed men approached Ivan. They were producing a project for David Lean. 'Yes of course,' Ivan knew about it. One man said, 'Can't get the funds. This town's closed. And this is David Lean who made 'A Passage to India'.'

After a pause Ivan said he was sorry and I thought he shivered for himself.

Jack Irish looked like those early breakfasts were doing him in. Or the Eves early evening. Of course it was age.

I noticed a man on his own at a nearby table and I thought I recognised him from the penthouse. Was he a bodyguard?

The waiters handed us the menus. Suddenly we were silent. Jack Irish didn't even open the menu but handed it back to the waiter.

'Eggs Benedict.' Then he looked from Ivan to me. Shit! Bugged!

Jack Irish stood up and said, 'Nice to meet you Mr Moffat. I think you owe the little lady some money.'

Ivan talked about it afterwards. He didn't believe in bugs. Or coincidence. He had a trouble with this one. He couldn't forget the look we both got. Jack Irish knew.

It was one deal we didn't get.

CHAPTER 21

THE INTERIOR OF JASPER BRETT'S apartment near Times Square offered a quiet I had not found in New York. It was as though a container filled with the air of a temple had been tipped into the space and stayed there. I breathed with ease. His objects were in the right places. 'I do meditation practise here,' he said. It was clean and sumptuous and Jasper kept it that way with love not obsession. 'I wouldn't live any other way,' he said. 'I like things to be at their best. I like my music to have the right setting.'

'What about people?' asked Silvio.

'I don't know about them.' Jasper came from the same part of Italy as Silvio's ancestors. Jasper's father, a bandleader, had brought the family to New York while he conducted dance bands at The Taft. 'That's where Silvio met my father. Silvio often ran a corner in the hotel for hard up artists and performers.'

'Your father was a good man,' said Silvio.

Silvio stood up defying the peace of the place and clapped his hands. Action came next. 'In minutes from now a guy will arrive. He's a traveller. And Jasper and I are going to talk to him in here. And you will stay in the kitchen,' he told me.

'And not come out,' said Jasper.

Ah so a drug deal. I didn't think that was Silvio's gig.

'If we need you we will ask you to come and meet him. You do know about Oxford?' said Jasper.

'Oxford?' So it wasn't drugs.

'You have a friend there,' said Jasper. 'A professor with children.'

'We met him when we were looking over the Randolph Hotel for the Evelyn Waugh series,' said Silvio. 'He was a historian.'

'Richard Cobb?'

'Don't worry her about all this,' said Jasper. 'It's just his brother wants to go and study there. He could be dying and it's his last wish and–'

'Oh do stop!' said Silvio. 'You have gone too far. She knows a professor of European history and that's it.'

'French history,' I said.

'Ca va.' And Silvio spread his arms, deal done.

The phone rang but only to offer Silvio a rehearsal date for 'Come Back Little Sheba' with Laurence Olivier, Joanne Woodward and Carrie Fisher. It was to be the first of three productions.

Jasper showed me the kitchen and it was his down to earth presence that reassured me. He seemed full of music and loved to dance and we would go to the best places that night. He loved atmospheres. Even if they brought warnings. He had always been like that. 'They can become a help to me. Even save my life.' He was in the reality of the moment or hour and that reassured me.

Silvio asked how I liked Jasper. So he had come into the kitchen smiling dangerously. 'You can tell he's been smothered by women. They all go for him.'

'When is your guest likely to show?' Jasper asked Silvio.

The bell sounded and Jasper went to the lift. Silvio got me juice from the fridge. There were many bottles of mixed water in beautiful neat rows. Everything was clear and reassuring. It was the last time I felt that.

I assumed this was a different arrival. No one man on his own with a dying brother seeking to experience Oxford. Everything was too much, too many voices and clanking motorbikes. Spinning wheels. The loudness and number of these men. The office door was shut and everything suddenly quiet. I found my door was locked from the outside. I could hear it was a business deal, quick and to the point and then it was done. Jasper opened my door slightly and waved for me to join him. The corridor, the other rooms, full of motorbikes and musical instruments. The office was busy with men of all ages wearing operational battle gear. They were covered in dust from miles of crossing the States. They looked briefly at me and then the tall one addressed Silvio. 'Is she your woman?'

For once I didn't have an answer. Silvio said I was the connection and knew professors at Oxford. He was smooth as ever.

'What about the main guy?' the tall one asked. 'One of these with more than two names like they don't make it out there with just one.'

'Hugh Trevor Roper.' The man was different. He had been to school and remembered it.

'He's a historian?' asked the tall one.

'The most well known historian,' said Silvio.

'He better be,' and the tall one moved Jasper effortlessly outside. The other men got to the door and claimed their motorbikes. They carried them down the stairs. Others took the lift. The tall one shook hands with Jasper, then Silvio. Then he handed Jasper an envelope and an old notebook. He reached the stairs before turning towards us.

'Let's hope the lady there was good at history.' He picked up his musical instruments and turned to Jasper. 'Let's meet for a blow Jas. I hear you're good on the horn.'

I waited till they left and the apartment returned to its usual silence. Then I spoke. 'What the fuck have you got me into now.' Jasper sat at the table and counted money. A lot of money. Silvio reached for the notebook. Jasper struck his hand, stopping him. 'No one touches that. My brother has a serious art gallery uptown. He said we can use the safe there while we book the plane.'

I said they looked familiar. 'Hells Angels?'

'That's right,' said Jasper. 'The real thing. The one with the name-dropping is so well known and he – Rusty Coones–'

Silvio stopped him. 'Don't need to overload the story.' To me he said, 'You never saw them.'

*

On the flight to London I understood I was in the middle of another Silvio improvisation and this time it could lead to death. I had to learn my lines and go out on the academic stage and I'd be rich for life. Silvio paused, 'Well a few years anyway.' He was always keen on straight talk concerning money.

Back in Kentish Town I felt I could think. And make a decision. The Hells Angels had approached Silvio with the diary of Hitler's mistress, Eva Braun, and he agreed to sell it for them. He needed to first get an endorsement from a well known historian and then put the diary quietly on the market to be auctioned. He would have to succeed because the Hells Angels down payment was substantial. Silvio chose Jasper Brett to negotiate and be the front man and I was the Oxford connection who would offer it to the historian for his paid information. I asked to see the diary. They refused. I wouldn't understand it. Why not? Was she so erudite?

'It's in German,' said Silvio. 'It's the real thing. Don't worry.'

I crept into Silvio's room and the notebook lay quite casually open on the floor beside his bed. It was in German with a more modern English translation attached to each opposite page. I read the first para. 'I awoke this morning and wanted to please the Fuhrer. So I put on my silk stockings with the seam on the back. He loves the feel of those stockings.'

I had to get out before the laughter burst followed. How

much did the Hells Angels pay Silvio to sell this? 70,000 dollars? Who in their right mind would believe the silk stockings tale? But who said Eva Braun could write?

*

That morning they talked one way and another about the division of money and decided to put it in a bank account to be opened in both their names. Silvio chose one in Kentish Town. Jasper preferred New York. We would take the train to Oxford from Paddington at noon. I wasn't at all sure if I could get directly to the prominent historian and decided to go first to my publisher Colin Haycraft at Duckworth's who I thought privately might buy it. If not I would go to Trevor Roper's brother the eye surgeon I had just met.

It started to go a little shaky when Silvio decided not to come. Suddenly he had to see Olivier about the Sheba play. 'You'll be better without me. She will come into her own then.' No problem there but what about him coming into his own with half that money. I didn't like it. He would not come. Jasper and I went to the Haycrafts for Colin to assess the diary. He said it looked like rubbish and flapped the pages. He said there were rumours that Hitler's mistress had kept a diary as far as he had heard but was this it. He said the content was probably written by a fourteen year old uneducated girl. He didn't even try to buy it or publish it. He gave it back. His hand putting the book into mine was a death sentence but he did phone the historian and I went to Oxford.

The eminent prof said a brief letter in acknowledgement of my knowing the background of this 'find' would be required. He saw me really in acknowledgement of my knowing the Cobbs. He handed the matter over to a junior colleague who first of all asked to photocopy the pages to check its veracity. Jasper refused and watched without blinking the handling of the pages. The colleague said if it was valid it would be in private ownership.

Our story of how we got it did not go down too well. 'Sorry to disappoint you.' And he handed the diary back. He did suggest the only way was to leave it with Trevor Roper so he could get an opinion on it. Or photocopy the pages leading to a less good opinion. I said to go for the latter. It was beginning to look like a nothing to lose situation.

Jasper and I sat in the old pub 'The Trout'. I used to go there Sundays with the Cobbs. I told him he'd have to give the money back.

He said he had debts. 'It's spoken for. I have to be positive. Maybe they'll come back positive and it will be published.' He was half right. A prominent member of the faculty did publish it sometime later, a little rewritten. It got notice but not all good. I did question why Oxbridge took it on.

Jasper still kept a copy of the diary. He was of the opinion that if you thought something was real hard enough then it was. Ivan said that was Hollywood. Not Kentish Town.

CHAPTER 22

I KNEW HE WAS IN town and the film prep would start in a few days. I thought he would call me. All my common sense told me not to call. I'd known him briefly and we'd had a few laughs. I felt I'd known him all my life. I phoned Ivan and he was busy doing some preparation about the Second World War.

'Jack's in town. He's starting Kubrick's 'The Shining'.' Ivan did hesitate. 'Look you hardly knew him.'

'But I knew him deeply.' Did I say that? Terrible mistake.

Another sigh. Two sighs. 'Jack Nicholson meets a hundred new people a week.'

'Where could he stay?'

'The Savoy.' And Ivan on the edge of giving lots of bad news called good advice said goodbye.

I saw the cover photos of Jack wearing the shades escorting a blonde model. Of course he would've lost my number if he ever had it. Feeling down now I talked to a clairvoyant. 'He and you are searching for the same thing. Clearness. Clarity. He does it chemically. You do it psychically.'

The phone rang with ordinary stuff. Then I gave up and Tom answered the phone. He handed me the receiver and said, 'This is for you.'

Jack said, 'Good day. I am a spider treater. Do you have any spare spiders I can take off you.' He said to come down. I asked when. He said now.

I went just as I was and the Savoy reception took me to his suite. The room was filled with busy people and he sat on a soft chair talking to a big black guy Caruthers who'd also been in 'One Flew Over a Cuckoos Nest'.

Jack said he was nervous and told me to feel his hands. Were they damp. He said his heart was jumping. He said he was very nervous of working with Kubrick. Kubrick might give the actress all the attention, the best trailer and then he Jack would know which way the wind blew. Then he said he was pleased I was there. A great smile. 'But you know that.' He introduced me as 'an old friend from long ago'.

'D'you fancy a snort?' he asked. I said I didn't.

'No,' he said thoughtfully. 'I know that.'

He did look different. Wired, busy, out of place. I told him to stay with all the success, all the awards. 'Think of that.'

'You're as good as your last film. You only make one bad film and that's it.'

Caruthers and others tried to cheer him up. He suddenly got his jacket and went to the door. 'The big one's in town. Let's go and see her.' He meant Diana Ross at the Hippodrome. I said something about my clothes being inadequate. 'Come on.' And he put his arm through mine and we walked across to the Hippodrome. It was a wonderful evening.

We stood together in the singer's dressing room afterwards. He suggested we meet the next day when he got back from the studio at 9 o'clock. We would have a quick dinner and go to Blake's Hotel where I understood he liked the models.

'You used to be a showgirl, so I'm told,' he said. 'At a pretty good club.'

'Yes. Murrays Cabaret Club.'

'What's it like now?'

I laughed and pointed up. Suddenly a crowd of friends

joined him. As I left he said, '9 pm Savoy. Tomorrow.'

＊

How many mistakes did I have to make? Just one. Silvio Narizzano.

I didn't see the mistake. I spent the whole day getting ready for the evening with Jack. It wasn't about leaning over a hedge and joking about spiders. I had my hair done, lashes, toes. Talked nonstop to anyone and everyone about Jack Nicholson. I didn't see it was a mistake, flaunting my luck in front of the 'have nots'. Silvio was going through a couple of bad moments himself. I didn't see he was even there. Yes he was certainly around when I chose the dress and bought the shoes. 'We have a date at The National to see the new actress,' he reminded me. She was good and came recommended for his second film with Olivier. Impossible. I had to be at The Savoy at 9 pm. I had to get home and ready.

So I was going to replace a valuable event to go on a dubious date with a movie actor? He insisted I must see the first act and say hello to the actress Kate Nelligan. He reminded me I still had a career to consider. Did I see it?

The first act? Did I see anything?

Jack epitomised Hollywood and stardom and all the riches I got from watching movies in my childhood. He was an alternative reality and closer than a lot of what was around me. I never tired of the pleasure of turning the pages of the film stars' annuals sent to me at Christmas.

Silvio insisted we go backstage to see her. I was now going to be late. I ran out of the dressing room up to the foyer. My undoing. The phone booths were ones without doors. I called The Savoy and got through to his room. I was aware someone entered the next booth. I told Jack I was at The National Theatre and would be 10 minutes late. He asked what was playing there? I said I was seeing an actress for a possible

129

production, Kate Nelligan.

'I hear she's good.'

Then a hand came round the open booth beside me and grabbed the phone. 'And I'm here.' I couldn't remember much about what was said. I was trying to grapple with him to get back the phone. Silvio did say, 'Don't get her all squiffy on drugs or you'll have me to reckon with.' I did scream at Silvio. He shouted back and flung me the phone. Jack said a couple of things. 'My private life is my own,' and then, 'goodbye.' He hung up. I remembered that. I rang him again and he said, 'Who is that man?'

'Silvio Narizzano.'

'I know of him. He made 'Blue'. Don't let him in my life.' He hung up. I remember a taxi taking me home.

'You alright m'am?'

I wasn't.

Did I fight with Silvio? Probably a dozen times. But later I thought I wanted to just disappear. He did say, 'You spent all that time on him. Your hair, your clothes, your shoes. Everything about him. It was as though you blocked me from your life.'

I blocked Silvio from my life.

It was more than just a Hells Angels escape with a dodgy diary. Silvio did the best he could. He got people to tell me it would never have worked out with Jack. He got his best producer to call me and say he wanted to make the film of my life in Spain with the antifascist lover and leader of his province. He knew 'Siesta' was coming out but this was the big one. He'd put an offer into my London agent. He wanted to start next week. I didn't need to ask who would be directing.

CHAPTER 23

SILVIO WAS SITTING AT THE wheel of a hired car just outside of Girona in Northern Spain and my Spanish love of many years stood on the roadside. I was as usual somewhere in the middle.

Silvio flung open the door. 'He's your past. I'm your future.' The engine was running. 'He's married. You won't give him the child he wants. You're too busy global traveling. That wife will give him all that.'

I was glad Jose did not speak English. I started to get in the car then Jose came forward and hugged me. I told him it would be a short film and I'd come back. He shut the car door gently and we started forward and I turned and he was still there. He waved.

Silvio talked about the film we were going to make. He had good ideas. Sometimes I forgot how good he was. He liked things lively. Even his driving spontaneous but he hadn't yet had any trouble. He drove north towards Cadaques and it started to rain. Then darkness and a strong wind and no lights on the road. He turned right because he could see what he thought was a lighted resort on the coast and the rain was forming huge puddles. I said we should stop at the next hotel. The darkness was complete and we couldn't even see the stars. No lights, no illusory resorts, just a road that had become huge puddles and he drove until water splashed to the roof of the car. Something was wrong. I could feel no road. I said to reverse and get out. This wasn't heavy puddle problems. He said he could see the resort with lights and continued forward. A surge of rain went high over the car and I pushed the door open against heavy water. This was no puddle. We were in the sea. I just got it open enough to get out. 'We're out in the sea.'

He jumped free and pulled our bags out and above his head he held them with one hand and my hand with the other. The water already came up above my chest. The crowd gathered on the shore and covered us with blankets into the nearest hotel. They said it was sure an unusual way to arrive in Cadaques. They gave us their best room, hot soup, hot showers, tea. They asked what I was doing. Yes what was I doing?

Silvio woke me at 3 am full of delight from looking out in the dark knowing our vehicle to death was still out there moving away slowly by the tide.

'I got an idea,' he said. 'It's good.'

As the daylight came through we sat on the balcony and made a profound and unexpected film story between us. The broken car now on the horizon seemed to draw the material out of us. It was Silvio beyond his best. The transforming vehicle washed by the gentle constant Mediterranean looked for a while like a baby's pram.

It didn't get written as a film but influenced a book I wrote a few years later.

What Silvio came with that dawn was brilliant.

We stayed on the balcony but daylight was fully there and changed the vehicle's spirit. It was now just a shape far out, could be a boat, or some drowned transport coming up from the sea bed. I agreed it was a symbol of our life. And he came with brilliance I had not yet seen. Looking at that dark shape out at sea, it now, that we nearly died in it, became not unlike an actual coffin and yes was a symbol of our life that could make all the rest worth it. I think I realised in these hours of changing light that within Silvio was a sadness he chose not to relate to and it came out as he made those outbursts of spontaneity, talent and trouble, never knowing the cause. It could be his way of dealing with loss. I understood in those hours of oncoming day that he always wanted children. He loved kids, wanted to bring them up and share their lives. Adults were just ruined children for him. Maybe this was why he lost it. Jump out of the pain he could not take.

And watching the sea and our transport to death, it seemed to demand something from us. A kind understanding. The black hulk did not want everything covered in false drama. We had been spared to tell the truth. Who and what were we? He helped me to write a farewell letter to Jose. 'What can you bring him? Only doubt and division.'

I seemed to be taken back to my first job in theatre at Colchester Rep. I had just come out of RADA and it was a time of anticipation. Harold Pinter, known then as David Baron actor lived in the digs which I took over at 30 shillings a week. One room, and share of amenities, run by Mr and Mrs Poulteny, a couple that lived on a scale of suppressed horror, zero to infinity. He had understood the glimpse he was given of how to deal with 'IT'. And he wrote about them and they influenced his plays and he gave them immortality. He would wait for my days off in London and waited while I bought Winklepicker shoes which he much liked and he would ask about the Poultenys and what they did and what they said. I hadn't got it. He asked me why I couldn't see him, the husband as he was. 'He didn't use words because they were for clever people. He's sizzling up like a pressure cooker near to exploding and she knows it. The outcome is up to her. She plays out his refusal to speak, his denial to join in.' Couldn't I see that?

So the drowning car unable to do its usual part in life brought us beyond our everyday words and joys and impetuous excursions that we said were 'creating'.

Pinter asked me to do a matinee performance of 'The Birthday Party' before it opened in London. I think I read from the script. It was surely the Poultenys of Colchester and all I saw there.

And in the interval he talked about reading it again but I was off traveling through Paris to Spain. 'I have to go to Sidcup.'

'Sidcup!' he exclaimed. 'What a beautiful word. It does not exist.'

'I used to live there.'

He could not believe it. 'Why are you going there?'

'I have to get my papers.'

Then I later saw the film of 'The Caretaker'. And the two lines were there. The guy says, 'I have to go to Sidcup to get my papers.'

I did see Pinter again when I went back to Murrays Club for a short while. He would stand by the exit door at 3 am and listen to the talk between the showgirls leaving and the clients waiting. Then we would walk down the centre of Regents Street which was empty and I was barefoot on the warm smooth surface. We would get an all night bus to Chiswick and a house of fellow actors. He wanted to know why the girls wore the pointed shoes, the Winklepickers. Why they refused one client to go to a hotel with another. Some went to the Covent Garden market for breakfast. Could I take him?

And then he asked about the Poultenys. Didn't I see the point of her hanging up her knickers on the line. Mr Poulteny accused her of putting them there to get the milkman 'at it'. It was a sign to the milkman all was free and he was out.

'Did she?'

Her husband said they were dirty unwashed knickers. Why were they on the line?

The rows that caused! He knew the under dialogue. I was too busy keeping away from the overt anger to bother with the subtext so what Pinter told me was I couldn't know what brought out the 'vehicle to death' on the horizon which I was certainly looking at that morning.

'So you have to go to Sidcup to get your papers?' said Silvio.

Sitting on the balcony in sight of that black shape I thought I'd better go to Kentish Town and get new ones.

AFTERMATH

SILVIO WENT ON TO MAKE some good films. One day he answered my phone in Kentish Town and a Buddhist retreat offered my son Tom a time there to get straight. Tom would not think of it. 'I'll come,' and Silvio took a train to Petersfield in Hampshire and stayed for over a year. He always returned there for short intervals.

Ivan had heard about 'the skirmish' on the phone with Jack but I knew and always had it would never have 'legs' as they said in LA. It would've been no longer than a short movie on how to swim with spiders.

The last time I spoke to Silvio he hadn't been off to some other life in Hollywood. He had been kidnapped in Spain for some weeks and saved by people from Kentish Town who got him out and he went to live with them. But I hadn't seen him and didn't know them.

One sunny afternoon the local police called me in Kentish Town and said they were holding a Mr Silvio – trouble with the name but I knew who they meant. 'He wants you to come and pick him up. He needs to get to a place by the sea.'

'What's the place?'

'It's Spain.'

The officer spelt CADAQUES.
I was the one in his life as he had once been for mine.

THE END

Milton Keynes UK
Ingram Content Group UK Ltd.
UKHW020230040524
442168UK00004B/155